ABOUT THIS BOOK

This book is part of a four-title series that explains our place on the Earth, the environmental problems we face, the kind of solutions we need, and how people are already working to put good ideas into practice.

Underlying the approach in the books is the Gaia theory, named after the Earth goddess of ancient Greece. The space scientist James Lovelock first proposed the Gaia theory in the 1970s. The theory suggests that the biosphere – the thin layer between the Earth's rocky surface and outer space, the home of plants and animals, including ourselves – is a living organism. Life has created and maintained the conditions it needs for its own survival. The Earth does not need the human species, but we may not survive unless we safeguard the natural resources on which we depend.

Another important idea is justice, or fairness. The brutal poverty experienced by one person in every four involves the denial of many basic interconnected human rights. Poverty on this huge scale is largely, although not only, the result of human choices and actions. Better decisions by individuals, small groups, larger communities, countries and governments can therefore make the world a fairer place.

Many of the most urgent environmental problems result from extremes of wealth and poverty. The very rich cause immense environmental damage by consuming too much, while the poor degrade their surroundings in the struggle to survive. Working to safeguard our environment and working for a fairer world are closely connected.

Raw Materials focuses on the natural processes and resources that are essential both to human society and to life itself, and considers the way we use the Earth's mineral wealth and the results of that use. The first chapter, **Energy and Elements,** describes our dependence on the flow of energy from the Sun and the Earth's fossil-fuel and mineral reserves. It explains, and suggests solutions for, a range of urgent problems: the effects of our activities on the Earth's natural greenhouse effect, ozone "holes", acid rain, and other forms of pollution. The second chapter, **Fresh Water,** explores the importance of rainfall and clean water in our daily lives. It looks at the severe water shortages experienced by people in many countries and how these might be overcome.

Each chapter contains information and ideas laid out in self-contained two-page sections, or "spreads". Each spread combines text, maps, diagrams, and photographs, and takes one of three viewpoints: Resources, Problems, or Solutions. Both chapters also include an illustrated "Gaia Watch" case study, provided by Oxfam, and two further features: "Do you know?" boxes provide additional facts, figures, and examples not contained in the main text; while "Home action" boxes suggest what we can do within our community to tackle problems.

At the end of the book, before the index, are three additional sections: an explanation of graphs, charts, and diagrams; a list of other relevant publications and CD-Roms; and a glossary of terms. We explain new, difficult, and important terms the first time they are used in the text: these terms are in **bold** if they appear in the glossary. Some terms, however, need a brief mention here.

We often describe countries as either "developed" or "developing" (although the terms do not fit all countries equally well). Developed countries are those where large-scale industry, based on burning coal, oil, and gas, is well established and usually the main source of jobs and wealth creation. These countries control most international trade and are generally rich. Developing countries are those where farming is still the main way of life. Most developing countries are poor. There are many more developing than developed countries. We also use the terms "North" and "South", broadly to mean the same as "developed", or "rich", and "developing", or "poor". All industrialized countries, apart from Australia and New Zealand, are in the northern hemisphere, while most developing countries are in the southern hemisphere.

We use the US dollar as the standard measure of money, which is common for international comparisons. As a rough guide, you can convert dollars to pounds sterling on the basis of $1.50 = £1.

Abbreviations
The following abbreviations are used in the series:

%: per cent	m²: square metre	g: gram
cm: centimetre	ha: hectare	kg: kilogram
m: metre	m³: cubic metre	t: tonne
km: kilometre	km³: cubic kilometre	kW: kilowatt
		kWh: kilowatt-hour

ENERGY AND ELEMENTS

"I . . . thought how wonderful God has created the Earth. And I looked out over my land, ripped up by human hands and machines. I thought: what will I get out of that dust? . . . . Nothing."

JOYCE HALL,
speaker for the Aboriginal people of Weipa, Australia, describing the mining of her people's land, 1981

Our planet is wonderfully equipped for life. The Sun provides heat and light; we have a constant flow of water; and on the planet's surface and buried underground are huge amounts of useful materials. We have used the power of the Sun – locked up in long-buried **fossil fuels** – and the Earth's **mineral** wealth to build modern civilization. But success has also brought failure. Excited by science and technology, we have forgotten the wisdom of not interfering with nature, and have introduced practices that we cannot properly control, with consequences that are not immediately obvious. We need to strike a balance between human achievement and nature's course.

Taking minerals out of the Earth can scar beautiful landscapes. Limestone is quarried in the middle of the Peak District National Park in England.

EARTH CARE

Raw Materials

Miles Litvinoff

Heinemann

CONTENTS

Editor
Judy Garlick

Designer
Malcolm Smythe

Managing editor
Lionel Bender

Art editor
Ben White

RAW MATERIALS (Earthcare)
was produced for Gaia Books by
Bender Richardson White, Uxbridge, UK.

This edition first published in Great Britain in 1997
by Heinemann Library
Halley Court, Jordan Hill, Oxford OX2 8EJ
a division of Reed Educational & Professional
Publishing Ltd
Oxford Florence Prague Madrid Athens
Melbourne Auckland Kuala Lumpur Singapore Tokyo
Ibadan Nairobi Kampala Johannesburg Gaborone
Portsmouth NH (USA) Chicago Mexico City São Paulo

Reproduction MRM Graphics, Winslow, Bucks, England

Printed in Spain

00 99 98 97 96

10 9 8 7 6 5 4 3 2 1

ISBN 0 431 07725 8
This title is available in a hardback library edition
ISBN 0 431 07724 X

British Library Cataloguing in Publication Data
Litvinoff, Miles
Raw Materials. – (Earthcare)
1. Raw materials – Juvenile literature
I. Title
333.7

Acknowledgements
Production: Kim Richardson, Susan Walby
Direction: Patrick Nugent, Pip Morgan, Joss Pearson;
Publisher Liason Hannah Wheeler, at Gaia Books.

Illustrations David Ashby; Norman Barber (Linden
Artists); Martin Camm (Linden Artists); Jim Channel
(Linden Artists); Stefan Chabluk; David Cook; Bill Donohoe;
Eugene Fleury; Chris Forsey; Aziz Khan; David Mallot; Gary
Marsh; Francesca Pelizzoli; John Potter; David Salariya;
Ann Savage; John Shipperbottom; Rob Shone; Nicky Snell
(Virgil Pomfret Agency); Clive Spong (Linden Artists);
Roger Stewart (Virgil Pomfret Agency); Alan Suttie; George
Thompson; Shirley Willis.

Photographs The publishers would like to thank the
following for permission to reproduce photographs: pages
4–5 Environmental Picture Library/Martin Bond. 6 Tim
Malyon/Oxfam. 11 Larry Boyd/Oxfam. 14 Jon Magno/
Oxfam. 16 Greenpeace/ NASA/Environmental Picture
Library. 17 Environmental Picture Library/Katherine Miles.
23 Environmental Picture Libary/Nigel Dickinson.
24–25(main) Geoff Sayer/Oxfam; (left) Rajendra Shaw/
Oxfam; (top right) Sean Sprague/Oxfam; (bottom right)
Jeremy Hartley/Oxfam. 29 ETSU. 30–31 Zefa/Weigl. 38–39
(all) Sarah Errington/Oxfam. 40 Jeremy Hartley/Oxfam.
Cover photographs Image Bank, Mark Edwards/
Still Pictures

Cover design Simon Balley Design Associates

*The publishers would like to thank Koos Neefjes, Amanda
Barker, and Fred Martin for their helpful comments on the
text. Bender Richardson White would like thank John
Stidworthy for help in planning the book, and Liz Clayton
and Anna Coryndon at Oxfam for producing the Gaiawatch
articles and supplying photographs.*

MILES LITVINOFF is a specialist writer and editor of books on
environment, development, and human rights for children
and adults. He works as an editor for the Minority Rights
Group, a human-rights organization in London, and tutors
the Open University Environment course. He is author and
editor of many successful titles, including *The Greening of
Aid: Sustainable Livelihoods in Practice* (co-editor, 1988),
The Earthscan Action Handbook for People and Planet
(1990), *Ancestors: The Origins of the People and Countries
of Europe* (co-author, 1992), the *Junior Cultural Atlas series*
(1989–94), and *The World Minorities Directory* (1996).

GLOBAL POWER-HOUSE

People who lived in ancient times worshipped the Sun. They were aware of its great importance in sustaining life on Earth. When, on a winter's night, you come home to a warm house and a cooked supper, you can do so because of forms of energy based on the Sun's power.

Solar energy is used in Nepal to heat domestic water supplies. In countries that have a sunny climate, or a difficult terrain, or that cannot afford coal- or oil-fired power stations, solar energy provides a valuable energy source.

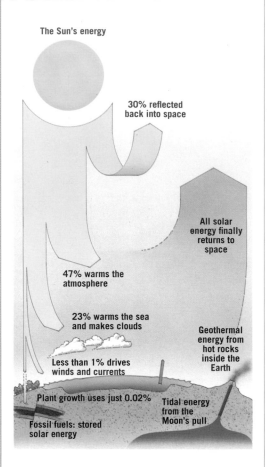

The Sun's energy

30% reflected back into space

All solar energy finally returns to space

47% warms the atmosphere

23% warms the sea and makes clouds

Less than 1% drives winds and currents

Geothermal energy from hot rocks inside the Earth

Plant growth uses just 0.02%

Tidal energy from the Moon's pull

Fossil fuels: stored solar energy

The Sun is the key to life on Earth. Without it our planet would freeze over, and all the animals that rely on its energy for plant growth and food would perish. Most modern comforts and conveniences – heating, lighting, cooked meals, television and radio – and many forms of transport from buses to jet aircraft, depend on our use of coal, gas, and oil. Their connection with the Sun is that they are fossil fuels, formed from decomposed prehistoric plants and animals whose life energy came from . . . the Sun.

Some people benefit much more than others from fossil-fuel energy. The average North American, for example, uses 280 times more than the average Ethiopian. And a lot of cheap electricity and petrol is wasted in **developed countries**.

Energy from the Sun
Solar energy warms the Earth's **atmosphere**, making winds blow and ocean currents flow. It heats seawater, which then **evaporates** into the air, falling later as rain. The Sun's energy also provides the "**fuel**" for plants to grow. Fossil fuels represent solar energy stored much earlier in the Earth's history. A little of the energy flow at the Earth's surface comes from other sources: the pull of the Moon powers the tides, and heat from the Earth's interior escapes as **geothermal** energy.

In contrast, millions of people in developing countries do not have enough fuelwood to cook a meal.

Another problem is that coal, oil, and gas are **non-renewable** and will not last for ever. We are using them up at a worryingly fast rate. And fossil fuels are dirty to use. Air **pollution** from burning them has created serious problems for the **environment** such as **acid rain** and **global warming**.

Fortunately, there are some alternatives to fossil fuels. These are **renewable energy** sources that use natural flows of energy such as sunlight, wind, rivers, waves, tides, and plant growth. Fuelwood is a renewable resource that is as old as history itself. Others have been developed recently and as yet are expensive to use widely. Even so, renewable sources promise clean energy and a means by which developing countries can meet their needs.

Some people include **nuclear** power as an important energy source for the future. Early hopes for nuclear power have faded because of the high costs of building nuclear power plants, fears about **nuclear reactor** safety after several accidents, and the problems of dealing with **radioactive** waste materials.

MAKING USE OF ENERGY

The pie chart shows how much of our energy supplies came from each main source in 1990, and how this may change by 2000. (The colours in the pie chart correspond to the base colours of the symbols.) Burning fuelwood and other plant and animal material was the earliest energy use. Then came sail power, which harnessed the wind, windmills, and waterwheels (using the flow of rivers). People first burned coal about 300 years ago, and oil and gas 200 years after that. Geothermal and **nuclear energy** have come into use only recently. As fossil fuels run low, we will rely more on renewable resources.

Oil is the world's main fuel source, providing 37 **per cent** of power. **Consumption** fell in the 1970s after price rises, but the use of oil is increasing again. We could run out in 45–50 years unless we conserve it better or discover new oilfields.

Coal is important in countries of the former Soviet Union and in China. They have huge stocks. Coal provides 23 per cent of energy, but it pollutes more than oil or gas. There is probably enough coal left to last several hundred years.

Natural gas supplies 18 per cent of our power. Cleaner than oil or coal, it is fast being developed. Eastern Europe and the former Soviet Union have huge underground gas fields. Yet there may only be 60 years' worth of gas left.

Non-renewable energy sources

  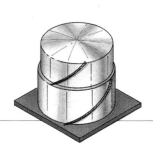

Renewable energy sources

▲ **Fuelwood and other plant and animal materials**, such as animal dung, were human beings' earliest fuels, and meet about 12 per cent of energy needs today. These are still the main fuel supplies for half the world's population, especially in developing countries.

World energy supplies

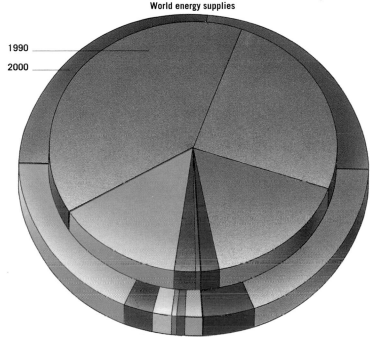

1990
2000

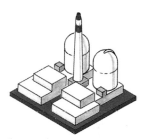

▲ **Nuclear power** is used in about 30 countries and supplies about 4 per cent of energy. It once looked as if nuclear power might solve the world's energy problems. But it is expensive, and people worry about health risks from waste disposal and power plant accidents.

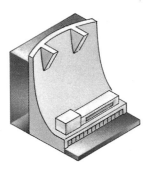

Hydropower provides about 5 per cent of our energy. Many rivers in developing countries are suitable for dams. Large-scale projects displace local people and take their land, as well as damaging the environment. Small-scale dams are often more successful.

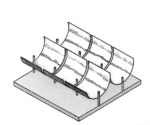

Solar (the Sun's) power is becoming an important energy source. Good modern buildings are designed to use the Sun's heat. Solar panels heat water, and solar cells convert light into electricity to power equipment and entire buildings.

Power from the sea includes wave power, **tidal power**, power from sea currents, and "**thermal energy conversion**", which exploits temperature differences at different depths. Tidal- and wave-power machines exist, but not on a large scale.

Geothermal power uses the Earth's internal heat, by pumping cold water down into hot rock or drawing up naturally heated water. The hot water is used to produce electricity or heat buildings. Several countries have geothermal energy systems.

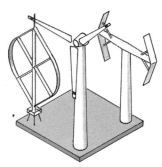

Wind power could be an important future energy source. Unlike traditional windmills, which ground corn, today's wind machines produce electricity. Wind-blown hills and coastlines are especially suitable for the generation of wind power.

ENERGY STORE

If you live in a centrally heated home, have warm baths or showers, and often travel by car, count yourself lucky. The cheap energy from oil, coal, and gas that we enjoy today became available only 100 years ago and may not last another 100. Hundreds of millions of people now and in the future will never have a share in our "fossil-fuel bonanza".

Differences in underground rock formation and the history of life on Earth have produced a very unequal share-out of fossil-fuel **resources** – oil, coal, and gas. Some countries have huge energy supplies; others have far fewer resources or none at all.

Owning fossil-fuel resources can be the key to great wealth, as the oil-producing countries of the Middle East discovered in the 1970s. A lack of energy resources is a serious problem for many countries in Africa, South Asia, and Latin America. But Japan has shown that a country can develop well without major fuel stocks.

Oil, gas, and coal will run out one day, even if we find new **reserves**. It will eventually become too expensive to look for new underground **deposits** and exploit them (bring them into use). It would be wise to conserve these non-renewable resources carefully and develop new, renewable forms of energy while we still have time.

DID YOU KNOW?

The true costs of drilling for oil
Oil and gas production can ruin people's lives. In Canada, for example, energy companies have sited hundreds of oil and gas wells on land that the Lubicon Cree Native Canadians own. Fuel drilling since 1980 has destroyed local animal populations and wrecked the traditional Lubicon way of life, which depended on nature. The 500 remaining Lubicon people have earned nothing from the $7000 million worth of fossil fuels taken from their land. Meanwhile, oil drilling in the Amazon rainforest in Ecuador has polluted rivers, killed wildlife, scarred the land, and brought misery to local people.

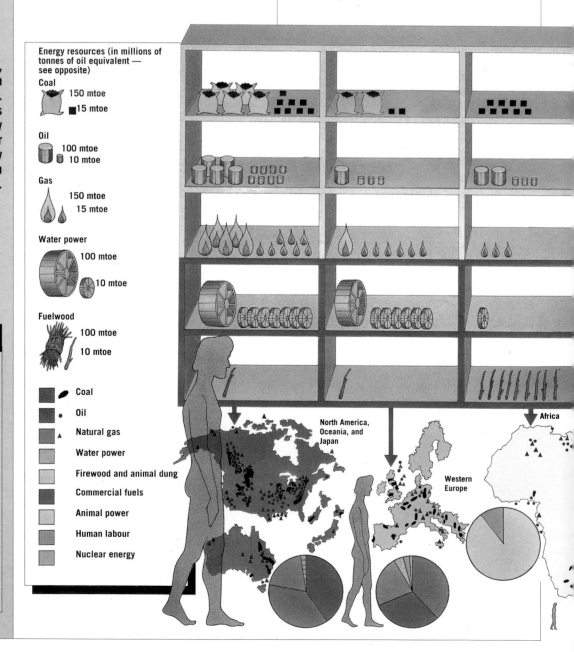

Energy resources (in millions of tonnes of oil equivalent — see opposite)

Coal — 150 mtoe / 15 mtoe
Oil — 100 mtoe / 10 mtoe
Gas — 150 mtoe / 15 mtoe
Water power — 100 mtoe / 10 mtoe
Fuelwood — 100 mtoe / 10 mtoe

- Coal
- Oil
- Natural gas
- Water power
- Firewood and animal dung
- Commercial fuels
- Animal power
- Human labour
- Nuclear energy

North America, Oceania, and Japan
Western Europe
Africa

Some regions are energy-rich, others energy-poor. Developed countries own two-thirds of coal, oil, and gas deposits, and use more than their fair share. The **Industrial Revolution** of the late 1700s and 1800s was based on coal and iron (another natural resource), and helped cause the split between developed and **developing countries**.

In North America, Oceania, and Japan the average person uses twice as much energy as the average West European, and 17 times more than the average South Asian. Western Europe relies heavily on oil **imports** from abroad, despite North Sea oil deposits, but it has reduced the amount of coal it uses.

Africa is fuel-poor, although Libya and Nigeria have oil, and South Africa has coal. Fuelwood and animal dung are the main fuels in much of the African countryside.

Eastern Europe and the former Soviet Union have large stocks of coal. The former Soviet countries also produce and sell large amounts of oil and gas.

The Middle East owns more than half of the world's known oil stocks and **exports** most of the oil it produces.

In Latin America, Mexico and Venezuela have oil, but other countries are fuel-poor. Some are short of fuelwood.

China mines vast amounts of coal but, despite a large population, relatively little fossil-fuel energy is used. Animals and human labour provide much of the power needed in China.

South Asia has only small fossil-fuel stocks. South Asians use very little energy on average.

THE WORLD'S ENERGY MIX

The top three shelves in the diagram show how much coal, oil, and gas people produce each year in eight world regions. The lower two shelves show the amounts of water power and fuelwood used. The maps show deposits of underground fossil fuels. The size of each human figure reflects the total amount of energy used by the average person in the region, and the pie charts compare the use of various energy sources.

The amount of energy produced from the various energy resources can be compared by using a measure (usually one million tonnes) of "oil equivalent". One million tonnes of oil equivalent (1 mtoe) produces the same amount of energy as, for example, 1.5 million tonnes of coal.

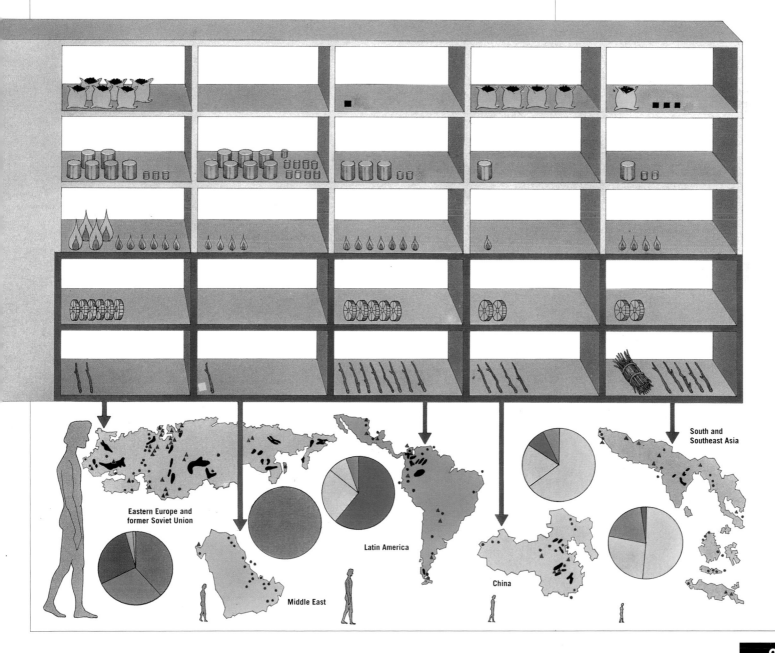

Eastern Europe and former Soviet Union

Middle East

Latin America

China

South and Southeast Asia

MINERAL RESERVES

Do you throw away your empty drinks cans? The lightweight aluminium they are made of may seem like rubbish. But to produce the millions of cans we drink from each day, parts of the Caribbean, West Africa, and South America have become mining wastelands, and vast amounts of fossil fuels are burned. Recycling cans reduces the need for further mining and fuel burning.

Minerals, ores, reserves, and resources
A mineral is any solid, non-plant, non-animal substance that exists naturally in the Earth's **crust**. An **ore** is a metal in its raw state, mixed up with rock, before people process it into a usable form. A mineral resource is the total amount in the ground, while reserves are the quantities of a mineral that we know we can extract by existing methods and use.

MINERAL RESERVES AND TRADE

The map shows which countries or regions of the world own reserves of 20 major minerals, and their share of world stocks. Two kinds of mineral are included: those that are available in large enough amounts to meet today's needs easily, and strategic, or key, minerals. These are defined as those minerals that are essential for modern industry, but which are in relatively short supply.

The map also shows how countries import (buy) and export (sell) mined and processed minerals in the world marketplace, giving as examples the trade in aluminium (**bauxite** is the **raw material**) and copper.

 Share of world reserves of minerals

 Share of world reserves of strategic minerals that could run low

 Bauxite (for aluminium) and/or copper ore exported (100,000 tonnes)

 Bauxite (for aluminium) and/or copper ore imported (100,000 tonnes)

 Aluminium and/or copper production for own use (100,000 tonnes)

 Aluminium and/or copper production for export (100,000 tonnes)

Since humankind first appeared on Earth it has used the planet's mineral wealth. After the Stone Age came the Bronze Age, when people made their tools from bronze, an alloy (a mixture of metals) of copper and tin. Next came the Iron Age, when people learned to work with iron mined from the ground.

Today we rely heavily on about 80 minerals, many of which are still available in large quantities.

Canada

USA

0.6

Mexico

Jamaica 84.7

15.1

18.7

67.3

18.6

Guyana

Peru 1.0

26.8

Brazil

1.7

Chile

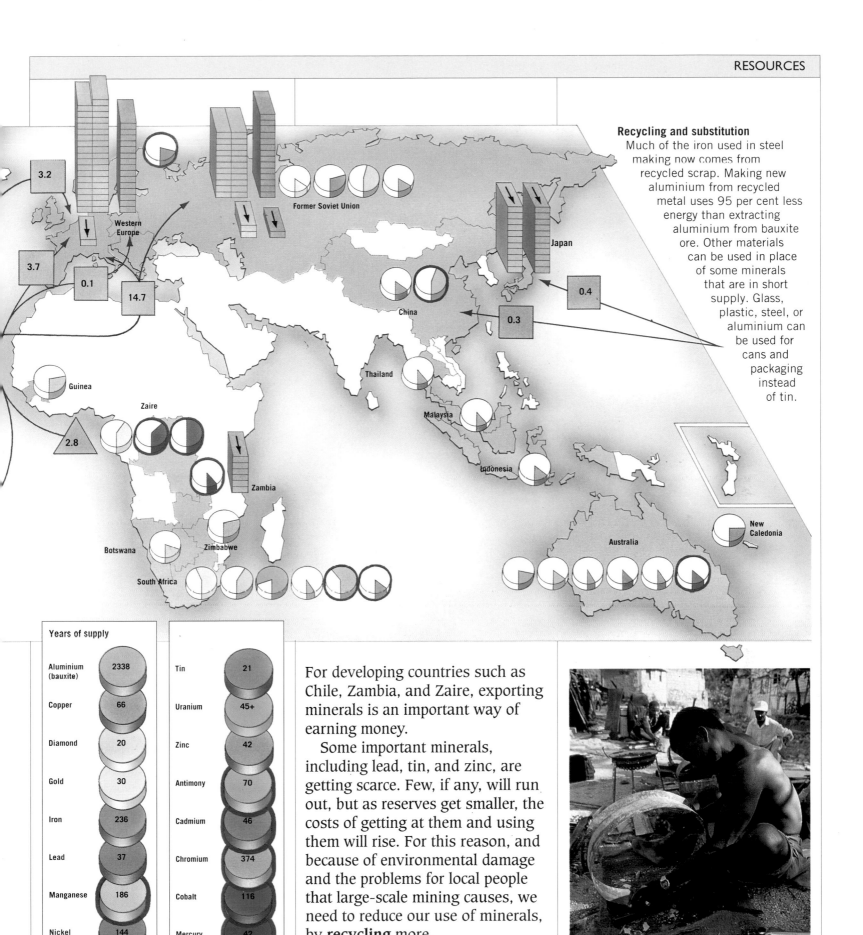

Recycling and substitution
Much of the iron used in steel making now comes from recycled scrap. Making new aluminium from recycled metal uses 95 per cent less energy than extracting aluminium from bauxite ore. Other materials can be used in place of some minerals that are in short supply. Glass, plastic, steel, or aluminium can be used for cans and packaging instead of tin.

Years of supply

Mineral	Years	Mineral	Years
Aluminium (bauxite)	2338	Tin	21
Copper	66	Uranium	45+
Diamond	20	Zinc	42
Gold	30	Antimony	70
Iron	236	Cadmium	46
Lead	37	Chromium	374
Manganese	186	Cobalt	116
Nickel	144	Mercury	42
Platinum group	176	Molybdenum	97
Silver	24	Titanium	138

For developing countries such as Chile, Zambia, and Zaire, exporting minerals is an important way of earning money.

Some important minerals, including lead, tin, and zinc, are getting scarce. Few, if any, will run out, but as reserves get smaller, the costs of getting at them and using them will rise. For this reason, and because of environmental damage and the problems for local people that large-scale mining causes, we need to reduce our use of minerals, by **recycling** more.

We can estimate how many years' supply we have of key minerals (left) by comparing current rates of use with levels of reserves.

Scrap metal that has been salvaged from wrecked or old cars is recycled to make charcoal-burning stoves in Port-au-Prince, the capital of Haiti.

FUEL CRISIS

Are you doing all you can to help avoid a future fuel crisis? How much energy do you waste at home, at school, college or work, or when getting around? If you leave lights on in empty rooms, go by car instead of taking a short walk or bus ride, or cycling, spare a thought for people who have to walk hours to collect fuelwood each day, and for the Earth's future generations.

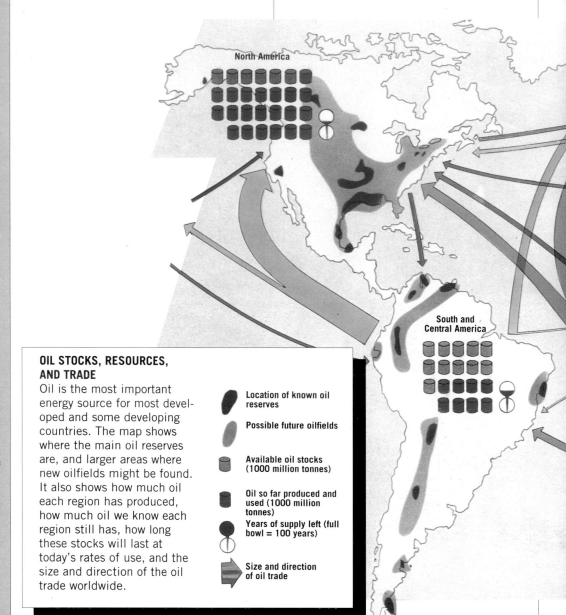

North America

South and Central America

OIL STOCKS, RESOURCES, AND TRADE
Oil is the most important energy source for most developed and some developing countries. The map shows where the main oil reserves are, and larger areas where new oilfields might be found. It also shows how much oil each region has produced, how much oil we know each region still has, how long these stocks will last at today's rates of use, and the size and direction of the oil trade worldwide.

- Location of known oil reserves
- Possible future oilfields
- Available oil stocks (1000 million tonnes)
- Oil so far produced and used (1000 million tonnes)
- Years of supply left (full bowl = 100 years)
- Size and direction of oil trade

DID YOU KNOW?

The future for coal
The world has burned as much coal in the 50 years since the end of World War II as people had previously used during the whole of human history. Of the three fossil fuels, only coal will be available in large amounts by the end of the 21st century. But burning coal is a major source of pollution. It is one of the main causes of acid rain and global warming, and is more polluting than oil or gas. So we would be unwise to rely on it in future.

For rich countries in the North, the fuel crisis began in the early 1970s and ended in the mid-1980s. In 1973 oil-producing countries of the Middle East raised the price of oil by three or four times. What had once been a cheap energy source was suddenly very expensive. Developed countries reduced their oil imports, changed to other fuels, and became more efficient in using energy. Many developing countries were not able to switch fuels or reduce energy consumption easily.

They were faced with rising fuel costs and falling prices for their own goods in a world marketplace that was in economic crisis. As a result, people in these countries suffered badly.

The price of oil fell back in 1986. Developed countries lost interest in **energy efficiency** and increased their use of oil again. Most developing countries have not been able to recover as fast. Supplies of oil will probably run out well before the end of the 21st century.

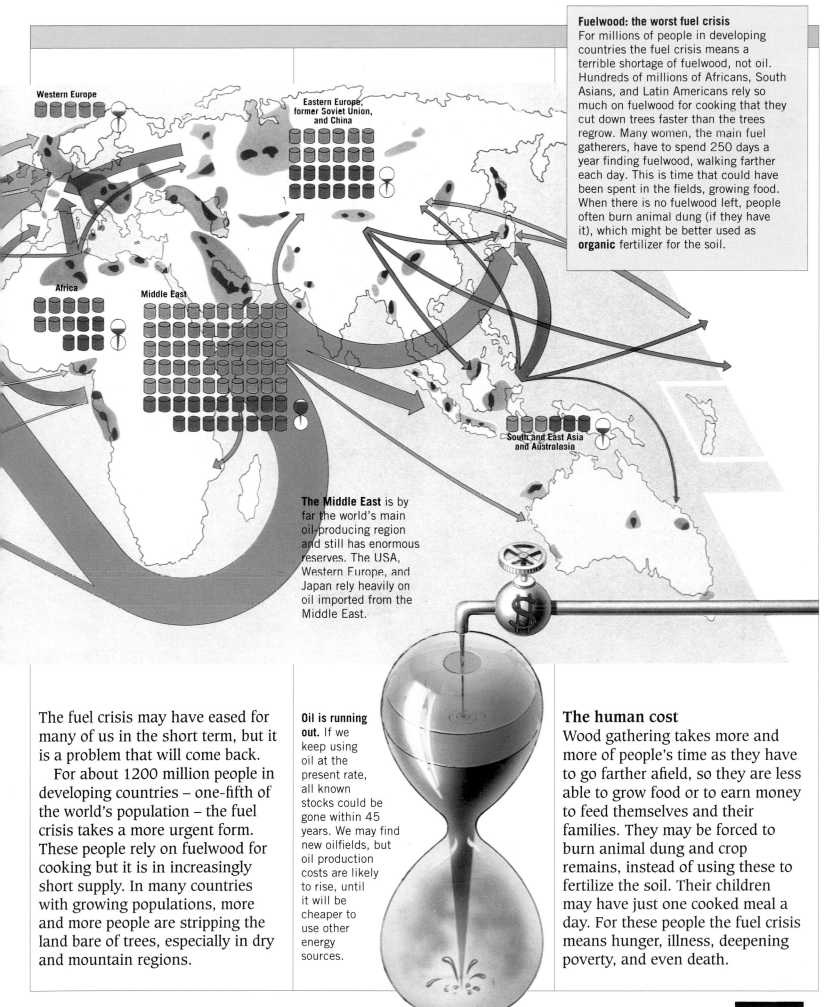

Western Europe

Eastern Europe, former Soviet Union, and China

Africa

Middle East

South and East Asia and Australasia

Fuelwood: the worst fuel crisis
For millions of people in developing countries the fuel crisis means a terrible shortage of fuelwood, not oil. Hundreds of millions of Africans, South Asians, and Latin Americans rely so much on fuelwood for cooking that they cut down trees faster than the trees regrow. Many women, the main fuel gatherers, have to spend 250 days a year finding fuelwood, walking farther each day. This is time that could have been spent in the fields, growing food. When there is no fuelwood left, people often burn animal dung (if they have it), which might be better used as **organic** fertilizer for the soil.

The Middle East is by far the world's main oil-producing region and still has enormous reserves. The USA, Western Europe, and Japan rely heavily on oil imported from the Middle East.

The fuel crisis may have eased for many of us in the short term, but it is a problem that will come back.

For about 1200 million people in developing countries – one-fifth of the world's population – the fuel crisis takes a more urgent form. These people rely on fuelwood for cooking but it is in increasingly short supply. In many countries with growing populations, more and more people are stripping the land bare of trees, especially in dry and mountain regions.

Oil is running out. If we keep using oil at the present rate, all known stocks could be gone within 45 years. We may find new oilfields, but oil production costs are likely to rise, until it will be cheaper to use other energy sources.

The human cost
Wood gathering takes more and more of people's time as they have to go farther afield, so they are less able to grow food or to earn money to feed themselves and their families. They may be forced to burn animal dung and crop remains, instead of using these to fertilize the soil. Their children may have just one cooked meal a day. For these people the fuel crisis means hunger, illness, deepening poverty, and even death.

GLOBAL WARMING

Have you noticed how, in the last few years, certain parts of the world have had hotter, drier summers, and others have had more frequent tropical storms than usual? Scientists predict that heatwaves and hurricanes will happen more often if the world keeps warming up. Nobody can prove that global warming is a long-term trend, but it looks more and more likely.

Without the natural "**greenhouse effect**", the Earth would be as cold as the Moon – too cold for life. **Carbon dioxide** and other gases in the atmosphere trap the Sun's heat after it has reached the planet's surface, preventing its escape. This heat warms the planet.

When people began to burn coal, and later oil and gas, it changed the composition of the atmosphere. As these fuels burn, carbon dioxide goes up in smoke. Cutting down trees, which take in carbon dioxide during **photosynthesis** (the process by which they make their food), and burning wood also increase carbon dioxide levels.

Activities that warm the world
Other human activities that release the so-called **greenhouse gases** include farming, coal mining, gas production, rubbish **dumping**, flying aircraft and driving vehicles, using air conditioning and refrigerators, and making **insulation** and foam packaging. Greenhouse gases include nitrous oxide, methane, chlorofluorocarbons (**CFCs**), and low-level **ozone**, plus carbon dioxide. The world has warmed by 0.5°C on average over the last 100 years. (The 1980s was the hottest 10-year period on record.)

The Earth has warmed and cooled several times during its history, and in warm periods there has always been more carbon dioxide in the atmosphere than during cool periods. So why worry? The difference is that previous warming has always been very gradual. However, at the current rate, the world could become 2.5°C hotter in just 100 years – too fast for many living things to adapt.

Sea levels are already rising as ice melts and as the water warms and expands. They could get 40 or 50 centimetres higher, flooding islands and low-lying coasts where millions of people live. Mild-climate zones might benefit from sunnier weather, but many food crops would not thrive in hotter, drier conditions. Many forests

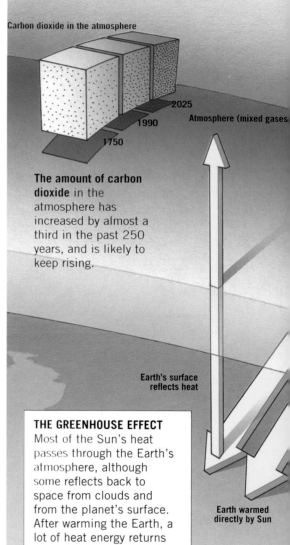

Carbon dioxide in the atmosphere

2025

1990

1750

Atmosphere (mixed gases)

The amount of carbon dioxide in the atmosphere has increased by almost a third in the past 250 years, and is likely to keep rising.

Earth's surface reflects heat

Earth warmed directly by Sun

THE GREENHOUSE EFFECT
Most of the Sun's heat passes through the Earth's atmosphere, although some reflects back to space from clouds and from the planet's surface. After warming the Earth, a lot of heat energy returns to space. But gases in the atmosphere also trap heat – like warm air is trapped in a greenhouse – and prevent it escaping back to space. This trapped heat warms the planet. Human activities add carbon dioxide and other gases to the air, adding to nature's own greenhouse effect.

would be reduced to scrubland or desert. Some animals would become extinct; and there might be more violent storms, as well as widespread diseases and pests.

Scientists advise us to reduce **emissions** of carbon dioxide and other greenhouse gases that we produce. Can we find a way to do this fairly throughout the world?

The Sun is nearly 5000 million years old, halfway through its life as a star. Although the Sun has grown slowly hotter, carbon dioxide in the Earth's atmosphere has decreased since life first began, and this balance kept the Earth's temperature steady until recently.

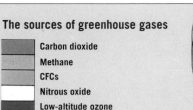
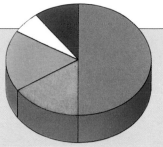

The sources of greenhouse gases

- Carbon dioxide
- Methane
- CFCs
- Nitrous oxide
- Low-altitude ozone

Carbon dioxide is the most important contributor to global warming. Its levels increase as a result of coal, oil, gas, and wood burning, and as we destroy forests. Methane levels are affected by rice cultivation, cattle rearing, coal mining, gas leaks, burning rubbish, and rotting wastepaper. Refrigerators, aerosols, air conditioning systems, insulation materials, and foam packaging include CFCs. Many countries have reduced the use of CFCs because they damage the important **ozone layer** in the upper atmosphere. Fuel and wood burning and the use of fertilizers release nitrous oxide. In strong sunlight, air pollution from cars, power stations, and factories produces harmful low-level ozone.

The effects of global warming

We cannot be sure how global warming will affect us in the future. Scientists on the Inter-governmental Panel on Climatic Change (IPCC) agree that the Earth could be 2.5°C warmer 100 years from now due to the presence of more greenhouse gases, especially carbon dioxide, in the atmosphere. This could cause sea levels to rise by 40 cm or more as the water warms and expands, and as **ice caps** and **glaciers** melt into the sea. Low-lying islands and coastal areas – such as parts of southeast England and Holland, where millions of people live – may be flooded permanently. Millions of people would lose their homes and farmland, and their supplies of drinking water. Changing temperatures and rainfall patterns could also mean that tree and grass species, including wheat and other basic food crops, no longer grow as well as before, so there would be food shortages and even widespread famine. Animals that cannot adjust to a quickly changing climate would die out. With warmer air currents in the atmosphere, storms will probably be more frequent and more violent. Tropical insects and diseases such as malaria and yellow fever may spread to temperate regions of the world.

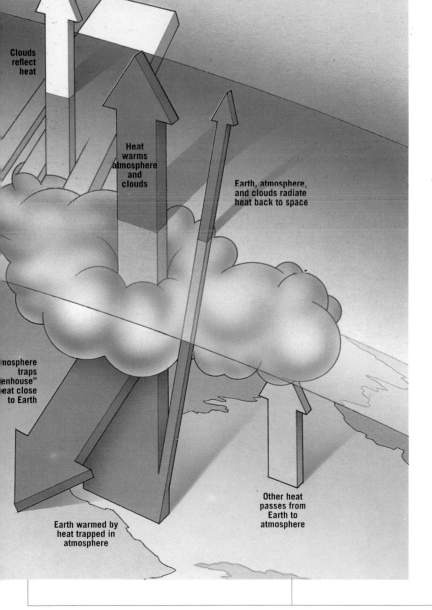

Heat from Sun

Clouds reflect heat

Heat warms atmosphere and clouds

Earth, atmosphere, and clouds radiate heat back to space

Atmosphere traps "greenhouse" heat close to Earth

Earth warmed by heat trapped in atmosphere

Other heat passes from Earth to atmosphere

Mount Pinatubo, *a volcano in the Philippines, erupted in 1991 and released masses of tiny chemical particles into the air. Scientists think these particles helped screen out sunlight, which could explain why global warming was less noticeable in the early 1990s.*

OZONE LOSS

Human-made chemicals called chlorofluorocarbons (**CFCs**) have damaged the **ozone layer**, 15 to 50 kilometres high in the Earth's atmosphere. This is the layer that protects the planet against high-energy **ultraviolet** (**UV**) rays from the Sun. Any damage to the ozone layer results in these harmful rays reaching the Earth's surface.

CFCs are used in refrigerators, air conditioning systems, spray cans, insulation materials, plastic packaging, and as cleaning fluids. The use of these machines and materials results in the release of CFC gas into the air, where it lingers for between 60 and 400 years. Other chemicals also act as **ozone**-destroying gases.

It is an alarming thought that a familiar household item such as a refrigerator can damage the environment and ultimately your health. Its cooling liquid may be one of the CFCs or HCFCs that in gas form damage the Earth's ozone layer, resulting in more cases of skin cancer and eye trouble. If we replace old machines with ozone-friendly ones, we can help stop the damage to the ozone layer.

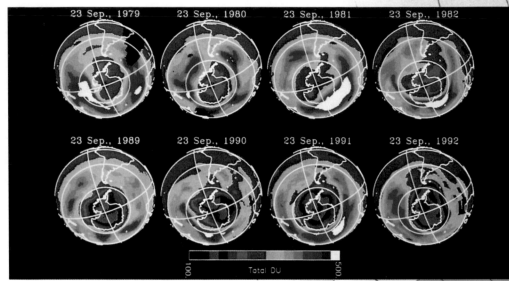

Damage to the ozone layer over Antarctica is visible in this series of satellite images. Red indicates the least ozone loss; yellow, medium loss; while blue, red-brown, and black indicate the worst depletion. By 1992 the ozone "hole" was as big as Antarctica (outlined in white). DU stands for Dobson units, in which ozone levels are measured.

DID YOU KNOW?

The Sun's rays can be deadly
Ultraviolet (UV) sunlight can cause skin **cancer**, including the deadly form known as melanoma. Other effects of UV rays include damaged eyesight and, possibly, weaker defences against infection. The US government has estimated that every one per cent of ozone loss causes thousands more cases of skin cancer each year, and blindness in 100,000 people worldwide. Ultra-violet **radiation** also harms plankton, shellfish, and fish, and may damage krill. Sheep have gone blind in southern Chile, and some frog species could be at risk as a result of damage to their eggs by UV rays. Food crops grow badly, with smaller leaves, if UV rays increase.

OZONE LOSS
The ozone layer has thinned during the last ten years. Thinning is worst at the poles during early spring, but the layer partly recovers in summer and autumn.

Ozone loss over 10 years

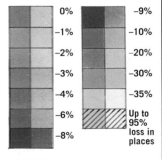

0%	−9%
−1%	−10%
−2%	−20%
−3%	−30%
−4%	−35%
−6%	Up to 95% loss in places
−8%	

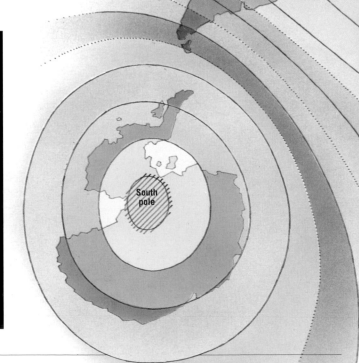

South pole

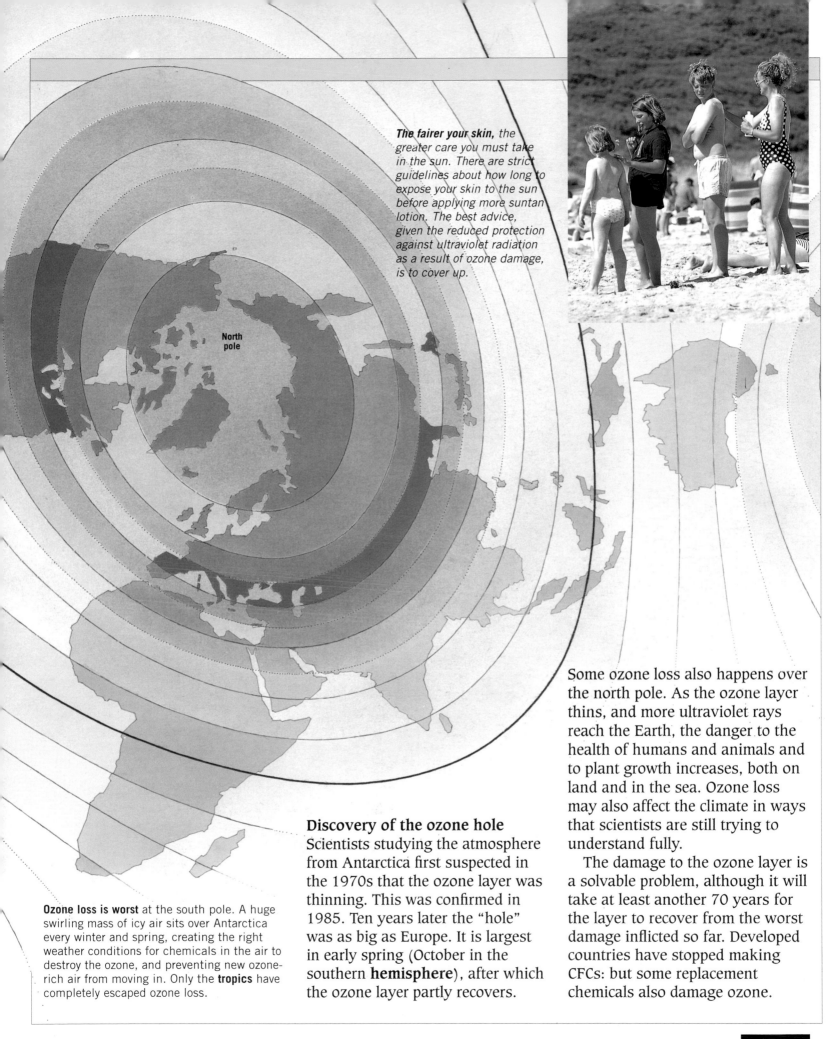

North
pole

The fairer your skin, the greater care you must take in the sun. There are strict guidelines about how long to expose your skin to the sun before applying more suntan lotion. The best advice, given the reduced protection against ultraviolet radiation as a result of ozone damage, is to cover up.

Ozone loss is worst at the south pole. A huge swirling mass of icy air sits over Antarctica every winter and spring, creating the right weather conditions for chemicals in the air to destroy the ozone, and preventing new ozone-rich air from moving in. Only the **tropics** have completely escaped ozone loss.

Discovery of the ozone hole

Scientists studying the atmosphere from Antarctica first suspected in the 1970s that the ozone layer was thinning. This was confirmed in 1985. Ten years later the "hole" was as big as Europe. It is largest in early spring (October in the southern **hemisphere**), after which the ozone layer partly recovers.

Some ozone loss also happens over the north pole. As the ozone layer thins, and more ultraviolet rays reach the Earth, the danger to the health of humans and animals and to plant growth increases, both on land and in the sea. Ozone loss may also affect the climate in ways that scientists are still trying to understand fully.

The damage to the ozone layer is a solvable problem, although it will take at least another 70 years for the layer to recover from the worst damage inflicted so far. Developed countries have stopped making CFCs: but some replacement chemicals also damage ozone.

AIR POLLUTION

In the laboratory we treat acid with extreme care because of the damage it can do. On a large scale, the effect of acid, even in a weak form, on trees, water, soils, animals, and buildings, and on human health, can be very damaging. Add to this all the other poisons that modern society pumps into the air, and we have a serious air pollution problem.

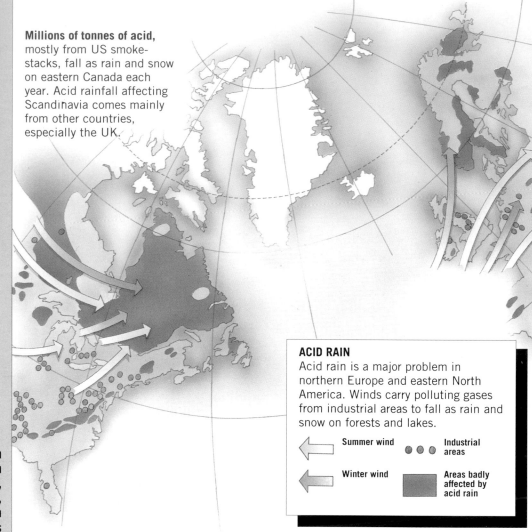

Millions of tonnes of acid, mostly from US smoke-stacks, fall as rain and snow on eastern Canada each year. Acid rainfall affecting Scandinavia comes mainly from other countries, especially the UK.

ACID RAIN
Acid rain is a major problem in northern Europe and eastern North America. Winds carry polluting gases from industrial areas to fall as rain and snow on forests and lakes.

⬅ Summer wind	●●● Industrial areas
⬅ Winter wind	Areas badly affected by acid rain

The air we breathe can be dirty and dangerous because of the pollution it contains. Power stations, factories, motor vehicles, and fuel burning in homes are the main causes of air pollution, which the wind can spread far and wide.

Acid rain

What we call acid rain is the pollution that forms when chemicals in waste gases from motor traffic and chimneys combine with water in the air. The acidic mixture falls as rain, sleet, mist, or snow, or as solid flakes. Northeast North America and parts of Europe suffer most, but the problem is growing worldwide.

Many Scandinavian lakes are lifeless. Their water is too acidic for snails, insects, birds, fish, or plants: only a few mosses, algae, and eels survive. Acid rain has damaged and killed millions of trees in North America, central Europe, Scandinavia, the former Soviet Union, the UK, and else-where. It also harms food crops.

Acid rain also eats away at the stonework of famous monuments such as the Sphinx in Egypt, the Taj Mahal in India, and St Paul's Cathedral in London, as well as the concrete of modern buildings.

Human health is at risk from all forms of air pollution. Heart and lung disease, asthma, cancer, and

Acid rain: causes and effects

Strong winds carry away sulphur dioxide and nitrogen dioxide which are produced as waste gases in the smoke from the chimneys of power stations and other industrial sites. The gases mix with water in the air to form sulphuric and nitric **acid**, which then falls as acid rain, sleet, and snow. **Acidification** harms trees, other plants, soils, rivers, lakes, fish, and other forms of water life.

reduced brain growth in children may result from it. Poisoned air in some industrial areas of Eastern Europe has caused deformities in thousands of children and increased **infant mortality** rates.

Waste gases from vehicles and factories often combine in strong sunlight to make a dangerous mixture of ozone and other chemicals that poisons the air.

Polluting waste gases

Power stations and factories

Acid snow on mountains

Waste gases mixed with water fall as acid rain

Melting acid snow damages soil and trees

Fish die in lakes

Lake-floor mosses survive but other water plants die.

Big-city smog

Cities suffer from **smog** (smoke plus fog) when polluted air, caused mainly by motor traffic, is made worse by strong sunlight, and cannot escape. Most famously, in Los Angeles, USA, in summer, a layer of warm air

lying over cool air and the surrounding mountains trap a mass of polluted air at ground level. The orange-brown smog damages people's health and plants in particular. Many other cities and industrial areas worldwide are affected by smog.

Smog alerts

These are now a fact of life during the summer in many large cities. In Mexico City the problem is so bad that people have considered using giant fans to clear the air. Air pollution in developing countries includes fumes from high-lead petrol burned in old, inefficient vehicles, and sooty smoke from coal and charcoal burning.

Some countries have begun to take action. In developed countries power stations have reduced waste gases, and cars use **catalytic converters** to clean exhaust fumes. Some cities have banned cars or factories; others run their buses on cleaner, plant-based fuels. These solutions are often too expensive for developing countries. We need a wide range of measures, from fuel efficiency to international agreements, to solve the problem.

Strong sunlight

Layer of warm air over cooler air traps smog

City of Los Angeles

San Gabriel Mountains

SPREAD OF POISONS

Is there any plywood, hardboard, or chipboard in your home? Products made from these cheap, handy materials often use glue containing formaldehyde. We now know that this chemical gives off poisonous fumes. Yet we still use it. Isn't it time we stopped adding poisons like formaldehyde to our environment?

HOME ACTION

Help reduce the spread of poisons and pollution.

- Use natural materials at home; wear natural-fibre clothes; do not use harmful chemicals.
- Use rechargeable batteries and fewer battery-powered items; non-rechargeable batteries leak poisonous chemicals after disposal.
- Buy pesticide-free organic food; grow plants organically in your garden, without weedkiller.
- Recycle your refuse and buy recycled goods; with less waste to handle, we can deal with dangerous waste better.
- Reuse plastic bags and other human-made items as many times as possible before replacing them.
- Report illegal waste dumping to the local authority.

POISONS IN THE ENVIRONMENT

Modern industry, including **high-tech** farming that uses many fertilizers and pesticides, has poisoned rivers and seas, soils and food crops, and animal and human food chains with chemicals that do not naturally break down or disappear. We dump vast amounts of dangerous waste in the ground, where some of it leaks into the soil and **groundwater**. Developed countries sell developing countries chemicals that they consider too deadly to use at home. Our bodies carry more and more traces of **carcinogens** (cancer-causing substances).

1 Modern industry produces ever-larger quantities and an ever-greater variety of dangerous chemicals. Many more metals are now known to cause cancer than was thought 50 years ago. PCBs, human-made chemicals used in the plastics and electrical industries, are very damaging to important organs in the body.

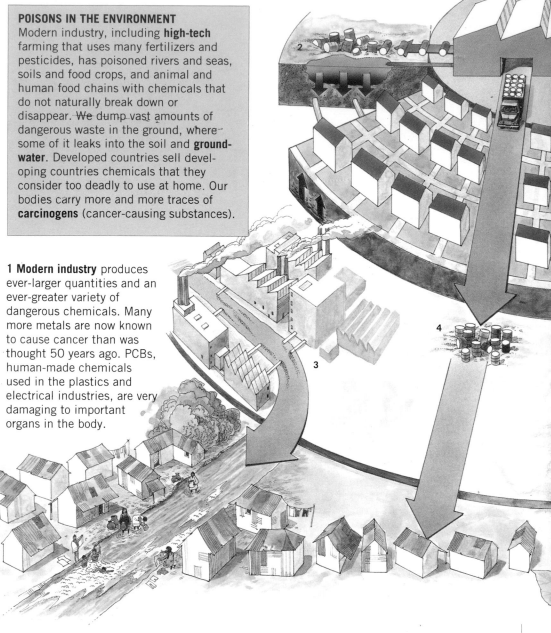

2 Dangerous wastes may leak from storage containers and poison the soil and water supplies. People living above an old underground waste dump at Love Canal, in New York State, suffered high levels of cancer and birth defects in the 1970s and 1980s. The national government declared the site a disaster area, and nobody can live there now.

3 Factory wastes pollute many rivers worldwide. But the situation is worst in developing countries where pollution controls are weak and people use the rivers as open sewers. Communities downstream often depend directly on river water for washing, drinking, and watering crops. People whose water is poisoned and polluted in this way suffer illnesses such as gastro-enteritis and more serious problems such as greater numbers of infant deaths.

4 Waste disposal is often cheap in developing countries and not as strictly controlled by governments. Companies in developed countries may try to gain from these low costs and lax controls by shipping dangerous wastes abroad, where dumping sites tend also to be badly managed. Companies in developing countries sometimes accept containers of deadly waste without knowing what the contents are.

Poisons in the food chain
River and coastal waters contain many human-made poisons. Filter-feeding shellfish and plant-feeding fish absorb metals, pesticides, and other deadly substances as they feed. The poisons stay in their body fat. When larger fish, seabirds, and sea mammals feed on the smaller species, the poison enters the larger creature's body. Human beings become part of the chain when they eat the larger fish.

8 Food crops that developed countries buy from developing countries can contain heavy traces of poisonous pesticides. African, Asian, and Latin American coffee, beef, fruit, and vegetables, for example, may be contaminated.

5 Pesticide spraying is often careless, damaging the environment and doing little to help the growth of crops. Pests can get used to a spray so it is no longer effective. When pesticides kill weaker pests – as well as creatures that kill them – stronger ones may increase in number, or new pests may move in. Farmers then need to use even more poisonous chemicals next time, which kill small mammals, birds, and other helpful animals.

6 Companies from developed countries often take advantage of weaker pollution laws and controls in developing countries to set up their more dangerous chemicals factories abroad. They also continue to sell to developing countries pesticides such as **DDT** and other products that they themselves have stopped using because of the dangers to health.

7 Pesticide poisoning harms or kills up to two million people each year – mainly in developing countries, where crop sprayers use the most dangerous chemicals, lack protective clothing, and often either cannot read or do not have instructions in their own language. The effects of poisoning include vomiting, diarrhoea, coma, blindness, brain damage, and death.

Dangerous chemicals from modern **industry** are poisoning our air, water, soil, and food, affecting animal populations and human health. Developed countries were the first to create chemical pollution, but developing countries, building up their industries and modernizing farming methods, are rapidly adding to the problem.

Some of the **toxins** (poisons) entering the environment do not exist naturally at all: most are long lasting and almost impossible to dispose of safely. Many of them enter the **food chains** of plants and animals after factories release them with waste water into rivers and seas. Others leak into under-ground water, or into the soil, after burial in containers and pits.

Chemicals in the body
Once these chemicals enter the body they threaten its health. "**Heavy metals**" such as nickel damage the nervous system, lungs, heart, and kidneys. **PCB**-type chemicals, used in electrical work, and many pesticides are linked with cancer, blood disease, and birth defects. **Dioxins** – products of paper bleaching, pesticide produc-tion, and burning plastic – also cause cancer; traces have been found in disposable nappies.

Most people living in developed countries have small quantities of these chemicals in their bodies. In Germany doctors have told women to breastfeed less because of dioxins in breast milk. The worst poisoning, bringing illness and death to thousands of people, has resulted from factory explosions such as those at Seveso in Italy in 1976 and Bhopal in India in 1984.

21

NUCLEAR DEBATE

There are beaches in Cumbria, UK, where some people think it is dangerous for children to play, although the danger is invisible. Near these beaches the Sellafield nuclear plant releases radioactive waste water into the sea. Some people argue that having nuclear-powered electricity is worth a few closed-off beaches, while still others believe there is no danger at all. What do you think?

NUCLEAR ENERGY WORLDWIDE

The map compares the number of nuclear reactors each country had at the start of the 1990s with the number they had ten years earlier. It also shows the relative importance of nuclear power as an electricity source in each country, and where the world's major nuclear accidents have taken place.

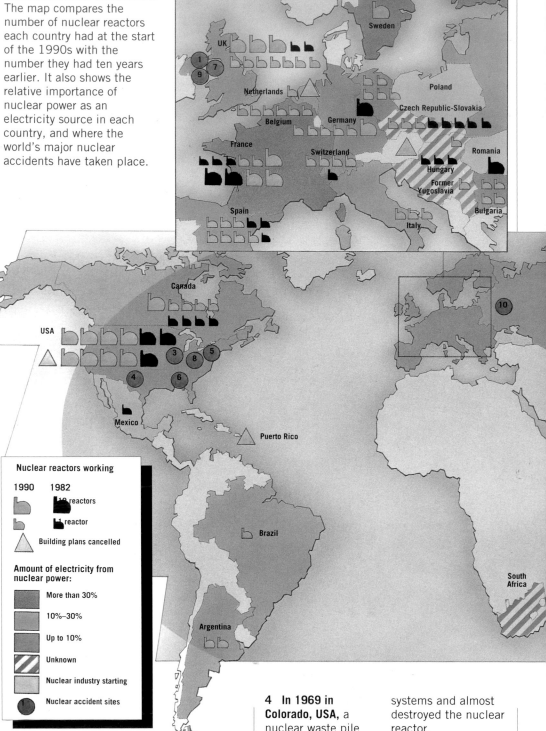

Nuclear reactors working

1990   1982

10 reactors

1 reactor

Building plans cancelled

Amount of electricity from nuclear power:

More than 30%

10%–30%

Up to 10%

Unknown

Nuclear industry starting

Nuclear accident sites

NUCLEAR ACCIDENTS

1 In 1957 at Windscale, UK, a reactor fire polluted 800 km²; 20 people died from cancer.

2 In 1958 in the Urals, in the Soviet Union, a nuclear waste explosion probably killed hundreds of people.

3 In 1968 in Detroit, USA, a reactor overheated and its core began to melt.

4 In 1969 in Colorado, USA, a nuclear waste pile caught fire, leaking radioactive dust.

5 In 1972 in New York, an explosion at a plutonium factory led to its closure.

6 In 1975 at Browns Ferry, USA, fire damaged emergency systems and almost destroyed the nuclear reactor.

7 In 1976 at Windscale, UK, 2 million litres of radioactive water leaked from the reactor.

8 In 1979 at Three Mile Island, USA, a reactor overheated and began to melt;

How long does radiation last?
The "**half-life**" of a radioactive material is the time needed for half its radioactivity to die away. The nuclear fuel plutonium has a half-life of 24,000 years. After 50,000 years it will still be deadly.

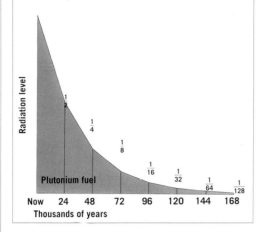

Radiation level

$\frac{1}{2}$
$\frac{1}{4}$
$\frac{1}{8}$
$\frac{1}{16}$ $\frac{1}{32}$ $\frac{1}{64}$ $\frac{1}{128}$

Plutonium fuel

Now   24   48   72   96   120   144   168
Thousands of years

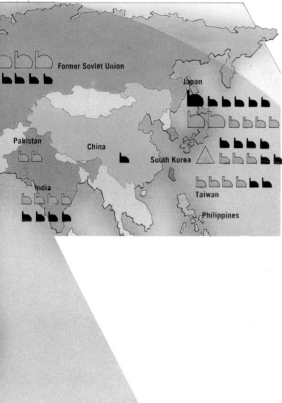

Former Soviet Union

Japan

Pakistan

China

South Korea

India

Taiwan

Philippines

Thirty years ago many people thought nuclear power would supply most of our energy needs. It seemed to promise cheap, clean, safe energy that would not pollute the air or use up fossil fuels. In the 1960s and 1970s France, Japan, the Soviet Union, the UK, the USA, and other countries built nuclear power stations. By the 1990s more than 400 nuclear plants running in 27 countries supplied more than a sixth of the world's electricity.

We now know that nuclear power will never produce low-cost or problem-free electricity. It has proved complicated and expensive to develop, with many technical difficulties. We cannot be sure about the health risks to workers in nuclear power stations and to people living nearby. Whether we can safely handle and dispose of **nuclear waste** that will be deadly for thousands of years, or safely dismantle nuclear plants when they are too old for use, is even more doubtful.

Then there is the fear of a nuclear disaster. The explosion at Chernobyl in the Soviet Union in 1986 killed thousands of people, ruined the health of very many more, and made huge areas of land unusable. Many nuclear plants in the countries of Eastern Europe need repair.

Some people also fear that terrorist groups will get hold of dangerous radioactive materials from the nuclear industry: both the generation of nuclear power and the **manufacture** of nuclear weapons use **plutonium**.

The nuclear industry still has its supporters, and some countries, such as China, still want to develop nuclear power. Yet, after years of pouring vast sums of money into the industry, most countries have stopped building new power plants. Sweden even plans to close down its nuclear industry completely over the next 15 years. Has nuclear power reached the end of the road?

France has 55 nuclear reactors, more than any other country except the USA, and produces three-quarters of its electricty using nuclear power. The Tricastin plant is in the Rhône valley.

radioactive gas leaked, possibly causing thousands of deaths among local people in later years.
9 In 1981 at Windscale, UK, leaking radioactive gas poisoned local dairy herds' milk.
10 In 1986 at Chernobyl, in the

Soviet Union, a reactor explosion caused the world's worst nuclear disaster. Radioactive clouds spread across Europe. Thousands of people in the area surrounding the plant have died from radiation sickness and related cancers.

PLANET-FRIENDLY ENERGY

Everything we do uses energy. At home we need energy for warmth and cooking. Outside we need it for transport, industry, farming, shopping, and at school.

Every household in the world uses energy, but they don't all use electricity or gas. Many use wood, charcoal, paraffin, twigs, leaves, crop remains, or animal dung. Homes in developing countries use much less energy than homes in developed countries. The average person in Ethiopia uses 280 kWh (**kilowatt hours**) each day, and in Pakistan, 2800 kWh. This contrasts sharply with 47,000 in the UK, and 128,000 in the USA.

In developing countries, people use many forms of energy, including people-power for pulling rickshaws and small carts or carrying loads, and animal-power for pulling ploughs, carrying loads, or turning water-wheels.

▲ *Animal-power* makes ploughing more efficient (main picture), and means farmers do not have to buy expensive machinery. Donkeys also pull carts to market, and animal manure is used as fertilizer.

◄ *Strange-looking objects are appearing* in many villages in India, often next to latrines. They are tanks for collecting waste from latrines and other waste, such as animal dung and leaves, which is mixed with water and added to the tanks. As the waste rots it gives off gas. The gas is collected in a second tank, and fed through pipes to where it is wanted. In this village, near Balgaum, families use the gas for cooking. The rotted waste is used as fertilizer.

We think of wind, water, and solar power as new technologies, but people have been using them for thousands of years. The sun dries clothes, wood, and pottery, and is used to dry foods to preserve them; the wind powers boats and windmills; and water turns water-wheels and transports timber. New uses are being found for traditional forms of energy.

Hydropower in Vietnam

Na Lang hamlet looks much like any other settlement in the Lao Cai district of Vietnam. It is high up in the mountains, surrounded by terraces of rice and vegetables. The houses have woven bamboo walls and roofs thatched with banana leaves. But there is a difference: the eight families living in Na Lang are using water to make electricity.

Near the hamlet is a small stream and in the bed of the stream are eight small **turbines**. As the stream flows down the mountain, some of the water is directed into a channel. This makes the water flow fast enough to spin the turbines which generate electricity. The turbines produce enough electricity for every household to have an electric light.

▲ *Fast-flowing mountain streams* are used to drive turbines – here being checked to make sure they are in working order – in this small-scale hydroelectric scheme in Vietnam.

◄ *In the Turkana District of Kenya,* windmills are used for drawing groundwater up to the surface. Rainfall is sparse, and the windmills provide a reliable source of water for people and livestock. Families from the surrounding area come here to collect water, to wash, and to water their herds of goats, sheep, and camels.

REUSE, REPAIR, RECYCLE

What happens to rubbish thrown on the ground? Metal cans take the rest of your lifetime to break down and disappear. Glass breaks into tiny pieces and then stays that way. Plastic will survive whole or in pieces for hundreds, perhaps thousands, of years. Shouldn't we dispose of these materials in a responsible way?

HOME ACTION

We can all help reduce waste.
- Reject goods in shops that are heavily packaged; try to buy items loose and unpackaged.
- Use refillable containers, for example for milk, and return them.
- Repair things instead of throwing them away: get your broken bike fixed rather than buy a new one.
- Look for recycled products, and choose materials that can be recycled easily.
- Give old furniture and other goods to a local charity store or repair workshop.
- Recycle all your paper, card, glass, metal, plastic, and textiles.
- Compost garden and kitchen wastes.
- Campaign for better local recycling facilities in your area, including doorstep collection.

Like all plants and animals, we use energy and produce waste. But the energy, once used, is mostly gone for ever, and most human waste is of no use to other living things.

In developed countries people usually consume more resources and produce more waste than those in developing countries, where poorer people make use of as much waste material as possible. Whole families collect, sort, and recycle rubbish for a living, often living on the dumps.

In the developed world we have become more aware of waste, and industries are recycling more materials. Car manufacturers now design vehicles with recyclable parts. Community recycling schemes have increased, and more businesses use recycled materials. Yet we still live in a "throw-away" society, buying new goods rather than second-hand ones, or rather than repairing old items.

The benefits of waste saving

Reducing waste will help solve problems of energy, pollution, refuse disposal, and jobs. If all US drinks containers were returnable, the USA would save half a million tonnes of glass and 50 million tonnes of oil a year. Of the third of a tonne of rubbish that the average Western European creates each year, most is buried underground (some is burned, giving off poisonous fumes). Yet recycling creates more jobs than dumping.

As customers and householders, and working together, we can do more. Industries should make products longer lasting and easily recyclable; governments can do more to encourage waste saving.

Recycling paper saves forests and energy and reduces the amount of greenhouse gases given off into the atmosphere. The world recycles only a quarter of its paper today: by doubling this amount we would free millions of hectares of forest from paper production. Some countries, such as Mexico, Japan, and the Netherlands, already recycle about half their paper.

Recycling iron and steel saves energy and water, cuts out mining wastes, reduces pollution by three-quarters, and creates thousands of jobs. The world makes a quarter of its steel, and the USA more than a third of its steel, from recycled scrap metal. Metal can be used many times, so in future we should be able to use recycled scrap for almost all our steel needs.

Recycling aluminium saves about 95 per cent of the energy needed to make a new soft-drinks can, so it saves money too. Today we recycle less than a third of the aluminium we use, but it should be possible to recycle more than three-quarters. If shops charged a deposit on drinks cans – as many used to do for glass soft-drinks bottles – aluminium recycling would increase enormously.

Sorting is the key to recycling. Schemes in North America, Western Europe, Japan, and elsewhere rely on people sorting their household refuse at recycling centres or for collection. Machines can help: for example, magnets remove scrap iron and steel. In developing countries many people depend on refuse sorting and recycling for a living, although this is unhealthy, low-paid work.

Job creation is an important benefit of recycling. Repair and recycling are cheaper and provide more work than **landfill** or the burning of refuse. In the USA more people work in recycling than in metal mining, and the recycling industry is creating more jobs worldwide. Millions of people in developing countries already earn their living by repairing and recycling, which is useful work that should be fairly rewarded.

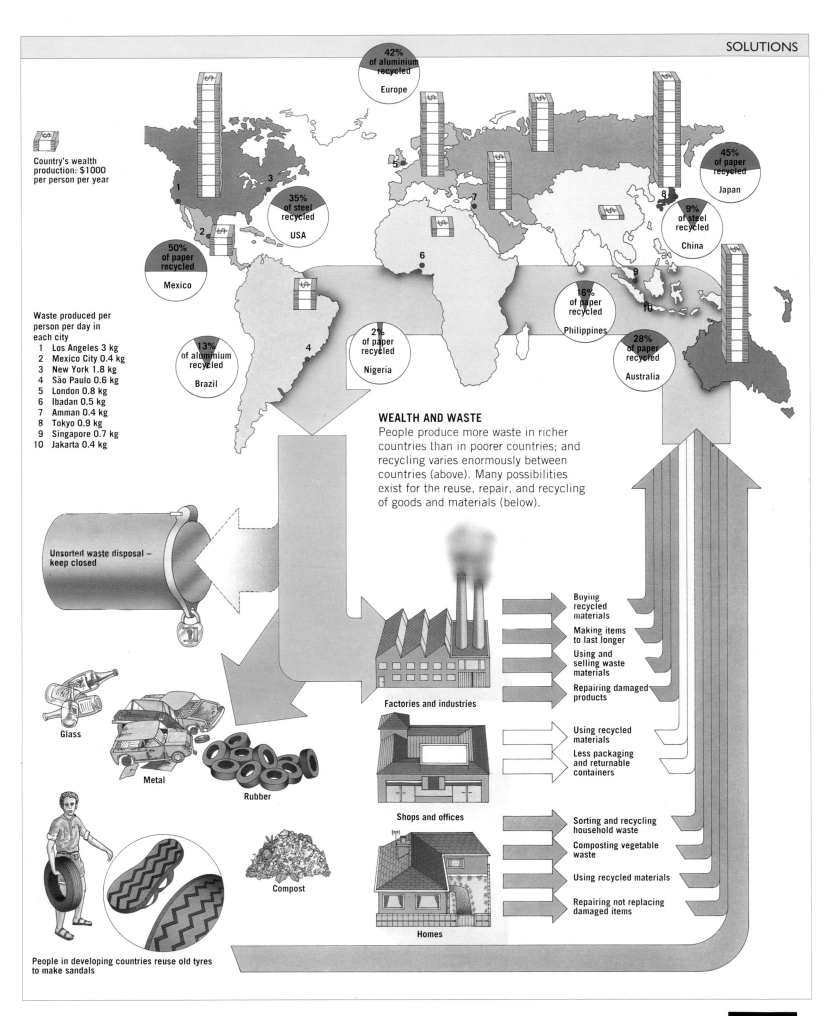

Country's wealth production: $1000 per person per year

42% of aluminium recycled
Europe

45% of paper recycled
Japan

35% of steel recycled
USA

9% of steel recycled
China

50% of paper recycled
Mexico

16% of paper recycled
Philippines

Waste produced per person per day in each city
1 Los Angeles 3 kg
2 Mexico City 0.4 kg
3 New York 1.8 kg
4 São Paulo 0.6 kg
5 London 0.8 kg
6 Ibadan 0.5 kg
7 Amman 0.4 kg
8 Tokyo 0.9 kg
9 Singapore 0.7 kg
10 Jakarta 0.4 kg

13% of aluminium recycled
Brazil

2% of paper recycled
Nigeria

28% of paper recycled
Australia

WEALTH AND WASTE

People produce more waste in richer countries than in poorer countries; and recycling varies enormously between countries (above). Many possibilities exist for the reuse, repair, and recycling of goods and materials (below).

Unsorted waste disposal – keep closed

Glass

Metal

Rubber

Compost

People in developing countries reuse old tyres to make sandals

Factories and industries

Buying recycled materials

Making items to last longer

Using and selling waste materials

Repairing damaged products

Shops and offices

Using recycled materials

Less packaging and returnable containers

Homes

Sorting and recycling household waste

Composting vegetable waste

Using recycled materials

Repairing not replacing damaged items

27

NEW ENERGY PATHS

Do you use a solar-powered calculator or battery charger? Such simple everyday items that make the most of pollution-free natural resources – in this case sunlight – show modern science and technology at their best. If only providing almost 6000 million people with the energy they need for living were equally simple!

The Earth cannot support increasing numbers of people burning more and more fuel. But people will always need energy for heating, lighting, cooking, and transport. Changing the nature and distribution of that energy use, and ensuring a fairer sharing of wealth so that people in the developing world can improve their living standards, could be humankind's biggest challenge yet. We need to switch from fossil fuels and nuclear power to renewable sources, while saving energy whenever we can. Where fossil fuels are in use, we need more efficient methods such as those which recycle waste heat, reducing the amount of fuel used.

Renewable energy sources, such as water power, wood, charcoal, and animal dung, provide nearly a fifth of the world's energy today. To increase this share, solar power, which works even on cloudy days, has to be further developed and its use extended. Millions of homes worldwide now have solar water heaters, and solar electric cells can effectively provide a power source for entire buildings.

From high-energy past to lower-energy future
We have used energy carelessly, building giant power stations and drilling new oil wells whenever we wanted more fuel or power. The challenge is to use far less energy, produced by means of the least polluting methods, to meet our needs.

The old way of providing energy (below, left) in developed countries and in some parts of the developing world depends on large power stations using fossil fuels, nuclear power, and hydroelectricity. We waste much of this energy, and create masses of pollution and "throw-away" goods.

The new energy path (below, right) will provide modern comforts but by means of energy-efficient and less polluting methods. Fossil fuels and large-scale power sources can be replaced by local, small-scale energy sources based on solar, wind, and water power schemes, and biogas.

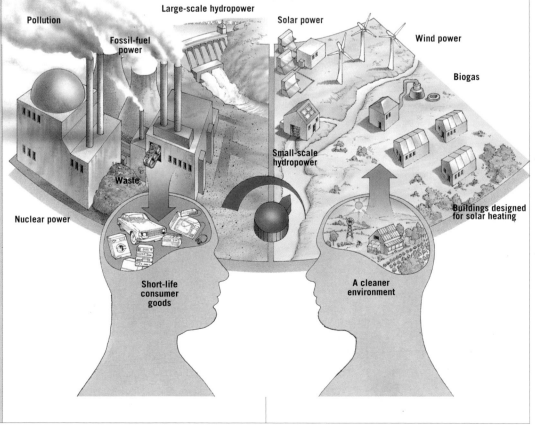

ENERGY SAVING
Our main areas of energy use are in the home, transport, and the world of work. In each area we can use energy far more wisely, conserving fossil fuels, reducing global warming and pollution, thus leaving future generations a planet worth living on.

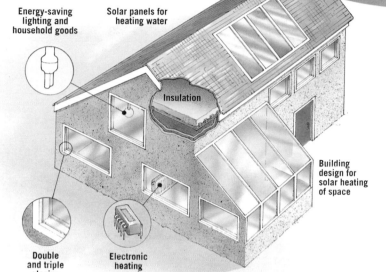

WORLD OF WORK

IN THE HOME

TRANSPORT

Factories, offices, and other work-places are now investing in ways of saving energy. Combined heating and power-generation (**CHP**) systems recycle waste heat, saving fuel.

Fuel-efficient cars, car-sharing and park-and-ride schemes

Energy-saving lighting and household goods

Solar panels for heating water

Insulation

Building design for solar heating of space

Double and triple glazing

Electronic heating controls

Carefully planned transport systems

Towns and cities encourage walking and cycling

More buses, trams, and light railways

Tomorrow's transport systems will make better use of efficient train, tram, and bus networks. Town planning will reduce people's need to travel long distances for work, shopping, and entertainment.

The Earth's natural heat can be used as a source of energy – geothermal energy. Hot springs occur where water heated deep in the Earth's crust comes to the surface. In some places the springs are close to towns and cities. In Lyon, France, geothermally heated water is used to heat homes directly, an energy-efficient system.

In the home we can quite easily halve the amount of energy we use for heating, lighting, hot water, and food storage. Energy-efficient lightbulbs use 75 per cent less energy than others, and well-designed modern buildings need almost no heating or cooling. The best refrigerators use only a quarter of the electricity other models need.

Making the most of alternatives
Businesses now know that energy efficiency saves money as well as reducing pollution. A low-energy lightbulb saves $30 a year. Car makers can build vehicles four times more fuel-efficient than the worst gas-guzzlers. Transporting goods by rail or canal, rather than by road, can bring huge savings.

In developing countries many people depend on fuelwood and need millions of new trees. Local people are best at protecting the forest: successes include village tree planting in Kenya, and a programme in South Korea that has reforested a third of the country.

Biogas is another major source of energy in the developing world.

Made from animal dung and human waste, it is widely used for lighting, cooking, and powering machinery. Other schemes include small-scale hydropower supplies and fuel from sugarcane and other crops. Renewable energy relies more on people than on costly equipment, creating jobs and suiting poor countries in particular.

FRESH WATER

"Of all our natural resources, water has become the most precious."

Rachel Carson,
US scientist and author
of *Silent Spring*

"Water, water, everywhere, nor any drop to drink" runs *The Rime of the Ancient Mariner* by Samuel Taylor Coleridge, reminding us that, despite all the saltwater in the oceans, we cannot survive without fresh water. Thirst is one of the most terrible ways to suffer and die. *Silent Spring*, a book published in 1962, first alerted us to the dangers posed to our water supplies by damage inflicted on the environment. Why is it, when we can explore the farthest reaches of the Solar System, and link all the world's cities by immensely complicated computer systems, that we can't ensure that every man, woman, and child on Earth has the safe water that they need for health and survival?

The magnificent Iguaçu Falls – on the border of Argentina and Brazil – demonstrate in 275 separate falls, divided by forested, rocky outcrops, the power and drama of the natural flow of fresh water.

CLIMATE & RAIN

Some people complain a lot about the weather, especially if it rains heavily on a day when they want sunshine. But regular rainfall is one of the best things that the climate can bring us – as anybody who has lived in drought conditions can tell you. If it rained a lot less, we might soon experience serious food shortages.

Temperature and winds vary around the world. The hottest regions are where the Sun is directly overhead, at and near the equator. Warm damp air at the equator rises and moves towards the poles, carrying heat and warming colder lands. Below this, cooler air moves towards the equator from the tropics. The direction of the resulting winds curves because the Earth spins.

Ocean currents are the result of winds, the Earth's spin, and the position of the **continents**. Carrying huge amounts of water, currents affect climate. The Labrador current flowing from the Arctic brings lower temperatures to northeast Canada. The Gulf Stream flowing from the Gulf of Mexico raises temperatures in northwest Europe.

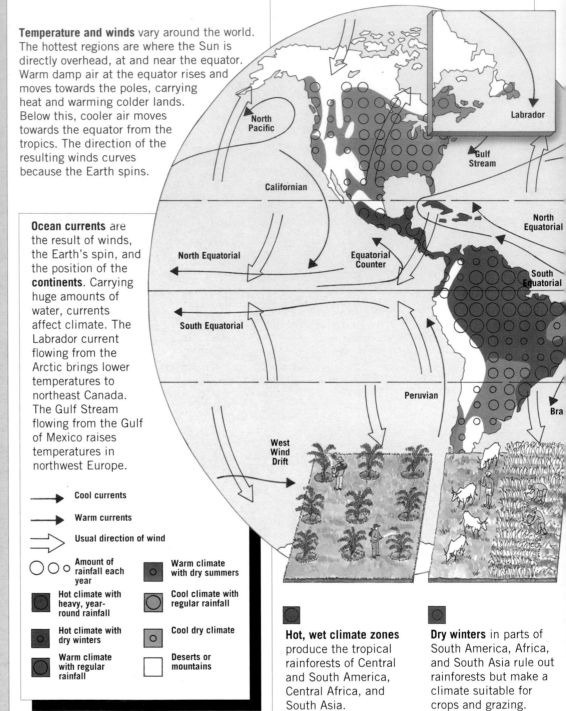

North Pacific

Labrador

Gulf Stream

Californian

North Equatorial

North Equatorial

Equatorial Counter

South Equatorial

South Equatorial

Peruvian

Bra

West Wind Drift

→ Cool currents

➡ Warm currents

⇨ Usual direction of wind

○○○ Amount of rainfall each year

Hot climate with heavy, year-round rainfall

Hot climate with dry winters

Warm climate with regular rainfall

Warm climate with dry summers

Cool climate with regular rainfall

Cool dry climate

Deserts or mountains

Hot, wet climate zones produce the tropical rainforests of Central and South America, Central Africa, and South Asia.

Dry winters in parts of South America, Africa, and South Asia rule out rainforests but make a climate suitable for crops and grazing.

Weather can change from one day to the next: climate describes weather patterns over a longer period. Climates vary around the world as the Sun's heat, winds, sea currents, and the frequency of rainfall affect each region differently. Climates have changed throughout the planet's history.

During the last ice age, 10,500 years ago, average temperatures on Earth were 2.5°C cooler than today – a lot in climatic terms.

The strength of the Sun varies according to latitude, or distance from the **equator**. The Earth is warmest at the equator, where the Sun is most directly overhead.

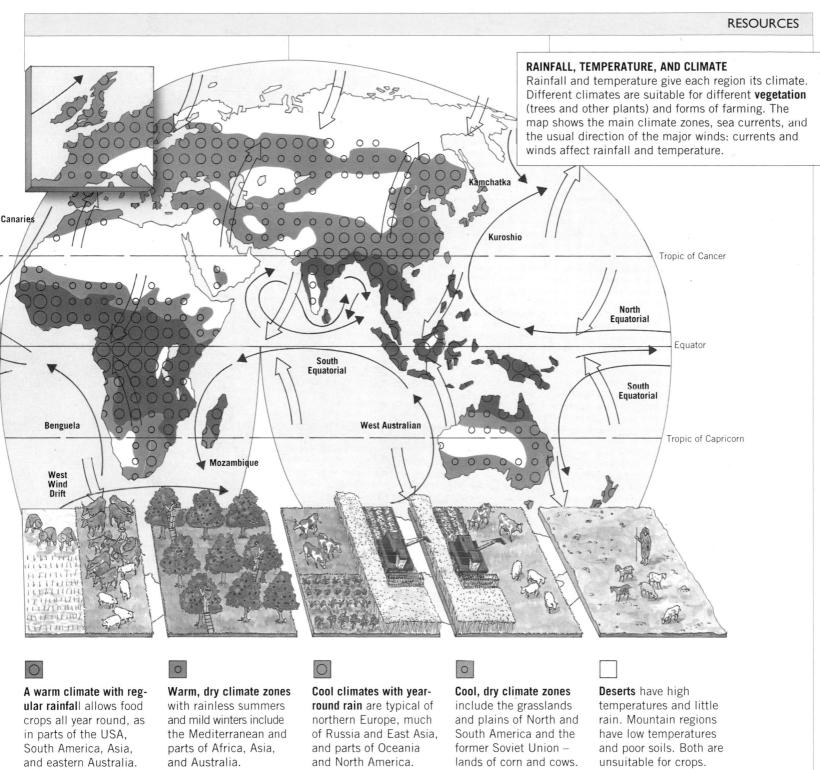

RAINFALL, TEMPERATURE, AND CLIMATE
Rainfall and temperature give each region its climate. Different climates are suitable for different **vegetation** (trees and other plants) and forms of farming. The map shows the main climate zones, sea currents, and the usual direction of the major winds: currents and winds affect rainfall and temperature.

RAINFALL, TEMPERATURE, AND CLIMATE
Rainfall and temperature give each region its climate. Different climates are suitable for different **vegetation** (trees and other plants) and forms of farming. The map shows the main climate zones, sea currents, and the usual direction of the major winds: currents and winds affect rainfall and temperature.

Canaries

Kamchatka

Kuroshio

Tropic of Cancer

North
Equatorial

Equator

South
Equatorial

South
Equatorial

Tropic of Capricorn

Benguela

West Australian

West
Wind
Drift

Mozambique

A warm climate with regular rainfall allows food crops all year round, as in parts of the USA, South America, Asia, and eastern Australia.

Warm, dry climate zones with rainless summers and mild winters include the Mediterranean and parts of Africa, Asia, and Australia.

Cool climates with year-round rain are typical of northern Europe, much of Russia and East Asia, and parts of Oceania and North America.

Cool, dry climate zones include the grasslands and plains of North and South America and the former Soviet Union – lands of corn and cows.

Deserts have high temperatures and little rain. Mountain regions have low temperatures and poor soils. Both are unsuitable for crops.

At the poles, the Sun's rays reach the planet at a low sloping angle, giving less heat. Winds – flows of warm or cool air – help to even out temperatures worldwide, as do ocean currents.

Water evaporates (rises in tiny droplets) into the air from warm seas and later falls as rain or snow.

The shape of the land affects rainfall. Warm winds carrying water **vapour** rise and cool when they reach mountains, releasing rain (which eventually feeds rivers). The winds continue as dry winds on the other side of the mountains.

Each climate zone has plants that are typical of that region.

They range from steamy rainforest trees to the small, sparse shrubs and mosses of the far north. Climate limits food production. Too much or too little warmth or water destroys crops and harms livestock. Low rainfall in the Sahel in Africa, combined with the effects of war, has led to terrible famines.

WATER RESERVES

Imagine a flood that covered all the continents on Earth with 80 centimetres of water. That's how much rain and snow fall on land every year. With so much fresh water coming our way, it seems impossible that we could ever be short of it. Yet because of uneven distribution and as a result of a variety of human activities, serious water shortages occur.

It is amazing how little of all the water on our planet we can use. Only a small fraction is fresh – the rest, seawater, is too salty for our needs – and much of the fresh water is permanently frozen or deep underground. Although about 40,000 cubic kilometres of fresh water (a massive 40,000 million million litres) flow from rivers and lakes each year, two-thirds of this disappears in floods or enters swamps and the soil before we can collect or save it.

There should still be more than enough for all the world's people. The trouble is that water is not always available in large enough quantities where it is needed. Canada and China, for example, receive similar amounts of rainfall each year, but China has 40 times more people. So each Chinese man, woman, or child has roughly 40 times less water for themselves than the average Canadian.

City inhabitants in developed countries use up to 50 times more water than villagers in developing countries. Most modern toilets, for

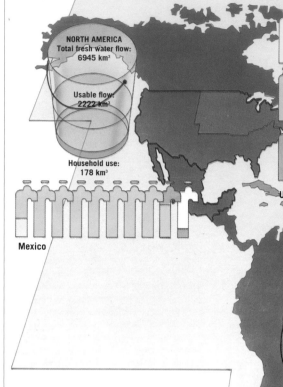

The main uses of fresh water are for irrigating farmland, for industry – as a cooling liquid, for cleaning purposes, and to water down pollution, for example – and for household needs such as drinking, cooking, keeping clean, laundry, dishwashing, and, in developed countries, toilet flushing, garden watering, and car washing.

example, use at least five litres of what is usually drinking-quality water each time they flush – as much as some people in developing countries have for all their daily needs. Millions of women and children have to walk for hours every day to fetch the few litres of water they need.

It is easy to take a steady supply of water for granted: but without it our health would suffer and our way of life could come to a halt. Farmland **irrigation** and industries that make plastics and paper consume huge quantities of water.

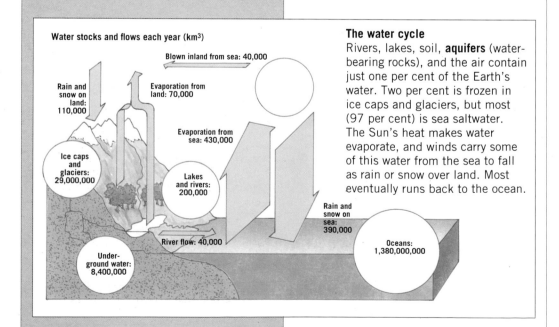

Water stocks and flows each year (km³)

Blown inland from sea: 40,000

Rain and snow on land: 110,000

Evaporation from land: 70,000

Evaporation from sea: 430,000

Ice caps and glaciers: 29,000,000

Lakes and rivers: 200,000

Rain and snow on sea: 390,000

River flow: 40,000

Oceans: 1,380,000,000

Underground water: 8,400,000

The water cycle
Rivers, lakes, soil, **aquifers** (water-bearing rocks), and the air contain just one per cent of the Earth's water. Two per cent is frozen in ice caps and glaciers, but most (97 per cent) is sea saltwater. The Sun's heat makes water evaporate, and winds carry some of this water from the sea to fall as rain or snow over land. Most eventually runs back to the ocean.

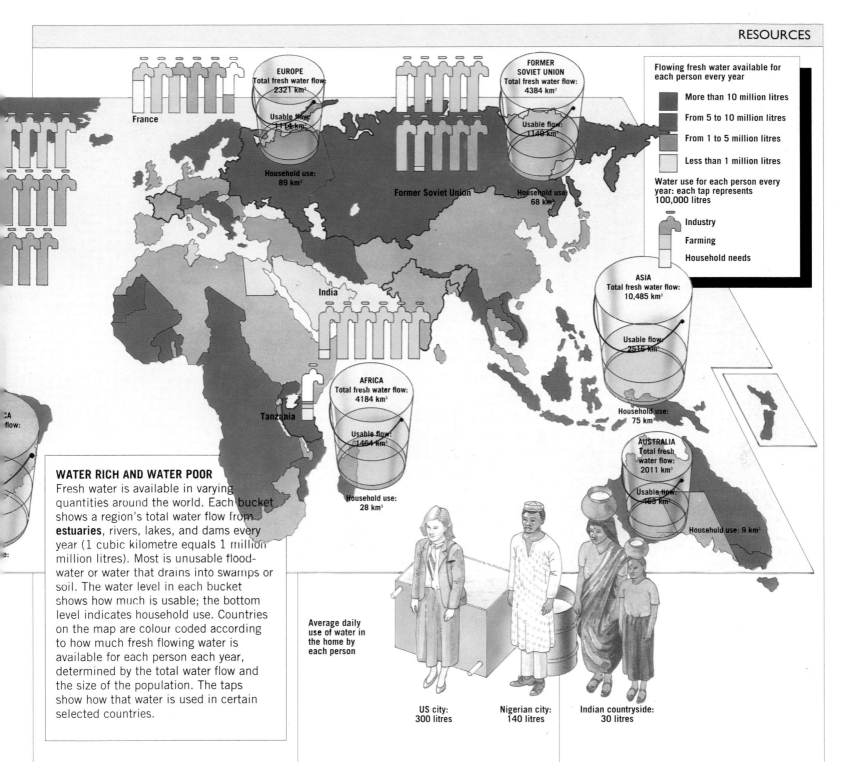

Flowing fresh water available for each person every year

More than 10 million litres

From 5 to 10 million litres

From 1 to 5 million litres

Less than 1 million litres

Water use for each person every year: each tap represents 100,000 litres

Industry

Farming

Household needs

France

EUROPE
Total fresh water flow:
2321 km³
Usable flow:
1114 km³
Household use:
89 km³

FORMER SOVIET UNION
Total fresh water flow:
4384 km³
Usable flow:
1140 km³
Household use:
68 km³

Former Soviet Union

India

ASIA
Total fresh water flow:
10,485 km³
Usable flow:
2516 km³
Household use:
75 km³

Tanzania

AFRICA
Total fresh water flow:
4184 km³
Usable flow:
1464 km³
Household use:
28 km³

AUSTRALIA
Total fresh water flow:
2011 km³
Usable flow:
483 km³
Household use: 9 km³

WATER RICH AND WATER POOR

Fresh water is available in varying quantities around the world. Each bucket shows a region's total water flow from **estuaries**, rivers, lakes, and dams every year (1 cubic kilometre equals 1 million million litres). Most is unusable flood-water or water that drains into swamps or soil. The water level in each bucket shows how much is usable; the bottom level indicates household use. Countries on the map are colour coded according to how much fresh flowing water is available for each person each year, determined by the total water flow and the size of the population. The taps show how that water is used in certain selected countries.

Average daily use of water in the home by each person

US city:
300 litres

Nigerian city:
140 litres

Indian countryside:
30 litres

Developed countries do, however, recycle a surprisingly large amount of water. More than three-quarters of the water that runs in our homes and factories may go back into rivers, from where we take it again, purify it, and reuse it.

The demand for water is increasing everywhere, and human activities are overstretching the available supplies in many regions.

People add to the amount of surface water by bringing up more from underground, some using traditional wells, others by means of modern pumping stations. However, "mining" water can be expensive and people often consume supplies faster than they can be replaced. Such sources may have taken hundreds or thousands of years to collect.

About 80 litres of water a day are – or perhaps should be – enough for the needs of the average person. But levels of water use vary enormously from region to region worldwide. In the USA average daily consumption in the home is 300 litres or more, whereas people in Madagascar use less than a fiftieth of this amount. Irrigation is by far the world's biggest water user, although the manufacture of plastics and other industries are also very "thirsty". Much of the water that we use in homes and factories flows back into rivers, from where it is taken again and reused: most irrigation water is never recovered.

WATER THAT KILLS

Do you drink tap water? Some people in developed countries worry about water quality and drink only bottled water or use a water filter. That may be wise. But let's not forget that in developing countries many people drink, cook with, and wash in water dirtier than that used in developed countries for flushing toilets.

DID YOU KNOW?

Where water is not on tap

In developing countries millions of village women and children have to walk for hours each day to fetch water from the nearest pond or stream. Poor people in cities are also badly off, queuing for hours in the street at public taps or buying water from private sellers at very high prices. In many cities in the developing world, richer people usually live upstream where water is relatively clean, while the poor live downstream and receive only dirty supplies for their daily needs.

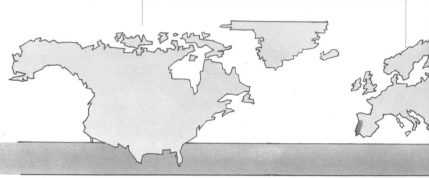

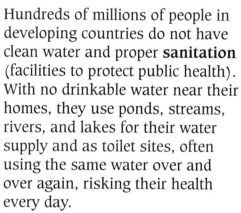

Many developing countries worked hard to provide safe water and toilet facilities for all in the 1980s, with support from the UN. But they could not keep pace with rising populations: by 1990 there were more people without clean water than 10 years earlier.

Hundreds of millions of people in developing countries do not have clean water and proper **sanitation** (facilities to protect public health). With no drinkable water near their homes, they use ponds, streams, rivers, and lakes for their water supply and as toilet sites, often using the same water over and over again, risking their health every day.

Unsafe water is the world's main carrier of disease. People who drink, cook, wash, and bathe using dirty water become ill with **malaria**, river blindness, cholera, leprosy, hepatitis, yellow fever, and a host of other serious infections. Insects, snails, and worms that breed in water spread many of these illnesses, which kill at least 25 million people throughout the world – including 15 million children – each year. Diarrhoea is the biggest water-linked killer, especially of young children, often through repeated attacks on the same person.

The countries of the world agreed at the United Nations in 1981 to make major new efforts over the next ten years to bring safe, clean water supplies and proper toilet facilities to all their people. Many countries, such as

Malawi in Africa and Bangladesh and India in Asia, made good progress. Yet, because of increasing human numbers, there were more people without water and sanitation in 1990 than there had been a decade earlier.

The problem is worst in the countryside, where many villagers live a long walk away from the nearest supply of often unclean water. But large numbers of town and city dwellers in developing countries are also badly off. In Cairo in Egypt, for example, 11 million people make do with water supply and **sewage** systems that were designed for a population of just two million. Many rivers in cities in developing countries are used as that city's main sewer.

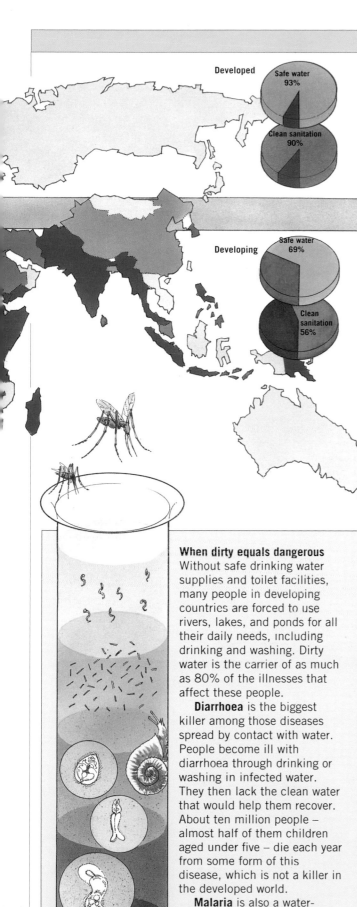

Developed
Safe water 93%
Clean sanitation 90%

Developing
Safe water 69%
Clean sanitation 56%

WHO HAS SAFE WATER? – THE NORTH–SOUTH DIVIDE

Percentage of the population who have safe water available

- 0%–40%
- 41%–80%
- 81%–100%
- No information

The map shows those populations that do not have adequate access to safe water supplies. The availability of clean water varies greatly across the world. Almost everyone living in developed countries, which are mainly in the **North**, has both clean water and reasonable sanitation facilities. In developing countries of the **South** nearly one person in three lacks safe water, and more than two out of five lack sanitation facilities.

Counting taps, not beds
Experts often count the number of hospital beds for every 1000 people to compare countries' health services. But the number of taps and toilets per 1000 people is probably a better indicator of the health of the population.

When dirty equals dangerous
Without safe drinking water supplies and toilet facilities, many people in developing countries are forced to use rivers, lakes, and ponds for all their daily needs, including drinking and washing. Dirty water is the carrier of as much as 80% of the illnesses that affect these people.

Diarrhoea is the biggest killer among those diseases spread by contact with water. People become ill with diarrhoea through drinking or washing in infected water. They then lack the clean water that would help them recover. About ten million people – almost half of them children aged under five – die each year from some form of this disease, which is not a killer in the developed world.

Malaria is also a water-related killer. It affects many millions of people and results in more than 1 million deaths

every year. Insects that breed in water, such as mosquitoes, spread malaria, yellow fever, and other diseases.

Contact with snails and worms that carry parasites and breed in unsafe water can cause infections in adults and children, killing one million people each year.

Hookworms enter the human body when the eggs are swallowed or when the young burrow through the soles of people's feet. The disease of the same name occurs where there are inadequate toilet facilities. Every year thousands of children in developing countries die from it.

Other illnesses that result from a lack of clean water include leprosy, cholera, river blindness, and scabies. These diseases, most of which affect the skin and eyes, do not usually kill but they harm the health of hundreds of millions of people.

The costs of unsafe water
Besides the great human suffering inflicted, a high rate of illness and death makes poor countries even poorer. India, for example, loses 73 million work days every year to illnesses caused by unsafe water, with the cost of medical treatment and lost production reaching close to $1000 million.

The deaths of many children in developing countries from water-related diseases encourages people to have more children than they really want, because of the fear that some of their children will die. This keeps families poor, harms women's health, and, if all their children do survive, adds to the problem of fast-growing populations in the developing world. This, in turn, prevents these countries from improving their living standards.

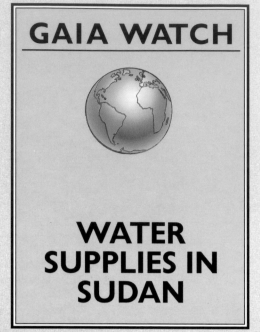

GAIA WATCH

WATER SUPPLIES IN SUDAN

Sheikh Issa Wintuk lives in Omeim, a Beja settlement in a valley in North Tokar, Sudan. The village is encircled by rocky mountains, jagged peaks, dry earth, and sand dunes. Acacia trees, shaped by the wind, are scattered through the valley.

In the past, wells were dug by hand. The walls often fell in, the wells dried up, and people then had to travel a long way to find water. Even when the wells were full, the water was rarely clean. People often fell ill.

Sheikh Issa Wintuk is helping to build a new well in his community. "We heard that Oxfam supported people in making wells for agriculture and domestic use, and we started a well, which you see us working on now.

I attended a hygiene workshop in Tokar, and learned that many diseases are caused by tiny creatures present in dirty water. When I got home, I told people what I had learned. It was clear that we must have a proper well and clean water."

▲ **This dry, wind-blown landscape,** with its sand dunes and scattered pockets of hardy vegetation, is typical of North Tokar in Sudan.

▶ **New wells** are being dug in several villages in the region. All new wells are lined with clay bricks to stop the walls from caving in.

The people of another village, Dolabiay, have built a well too. They are using water from the well for irrigation to grow food. They needed a pump, and someone to keep it running. Mohammed Ahmed El Haj was chosen to go on a course: "I have been trained to maintain the water pump. I know how to take apart and reassemble a pump, as well as maintaining it."

Not so long ago, the Beja were pastoralists, dependent on cattle, camels, sheep, and goats. They were nomads, travelling great distances away from their settlements in search of pasture and water. Now, some families still have animals, but only the men travel with them; women and children stay in the villages. Many people have decided that there are advantages in living in a settled community: better water supplies, health care, schools, and training for adults. But, in other countries, pastoralists have been forced by governments to give up their traditional way of life without such community support.

▼ **The establishment of a supply of water** encourages permanent settlement. Hadlul Ahmed Adam is in his family vegetable garden in Khor Baraka. The family grow melons, okra, and millet.

▼ **Women and children** from Belgigio settlement gather at the new communal well to wash clothes.

WISE USE OF WATER

Do you let the tap run all the time when you brush your teeth, or only as you need water? Turning it off may not make much difference to the total amount of water you use each day, but if everybody did the same, it would reduce water consumption significantly. It is also a way to remember how important water is and the wisdom of using it more carefully.

Water is piped from spring to village in bamboo tubes in Java, Indonesia. When villagers have taken all they need, they put a stopper in the end of the pipe so no water is wasted.

MANAGING WATER BETTER
Our use of water is likely to increase. Careful water management will help us meet tomorrow's needs. New dams, computerized monitoring of supplies, less wasteful crop irrigation, more water recycling, the replacement of leaking supply systems, and the use of water-efficient equipment will all be important. We will also need to use water less wastefully in our daily lives.

River dams (1) help control flooding and store water. But large dams can bring large problems, including increases in water-related diseases around the lake and irrigation channels. Small dams are often better.

Computerized monitoring (2), linked to satellite systems, can provide up-to-date information on floods and water pollution.

Water shortages and wastage, and the lack of clean supplies in developing countries, are serious and sometimes connected problems. People without enough clean water may live near large farms that use water wastefully when irrigating land. Governments of developing countries could help to manage supplies better by preventing big water users – farms and factories – from taking more than their fair share, as well as helping to provide villages with the safe water supplies and sanitation they need.

"Drip-feed" irrigation (3) is a low-waste method of keeping food crops well watered by the release of small amounts of water directly to parts of the plant that need it. Other irrigation systems waste up to 70 per cent of water used. Farmers can irrigate crops less wastefully by employing more people to work on the land.

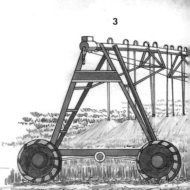

Health education helps people make the best use of clean water supplies and toilet facilities once these are working.

Involving local people in setting up and running water and sanitation schemes gives them the best chance of success.

Money in the hands of local people often solves sanitation problems better than money controlled by government.

Better health results from clean water and sanitation schemes, which reduce both the risks and the costs of disease.

Fewer children become ill and die where there is clean water and good sanitation. We could save millions more young lives.

Populations grow more slowly if more children survive. People do not need to have more children in case some die.

Clean water for health

It would cost less than the world spends on weapons every two months to give everybody on the planet clean water and sanitation. The diagram shows three important conditions needed for successful water and sanitation schemes, and three major results of schemes such as these in developing countries.

These schemes can do more to improve people's health than building new hospitals.

Villagers often need health education as well as clean water. Schemes usually work best when local people play a role in deciding where to set up wells and pumps, help to build and keep them in working order, as well as controlling the money involved.

Low-cost toilets, including composting ones that turn human waste into clean, useful fertilizer, often work better and are easier to repair than expensive piped sewage systems. The main results of improvements in water supply and sanitation include better health, fewer child deaths, and ultimately slower population growth.

Old, leaking supply systems in cities (4) waste a lot of water, and need replacing. Also, we need more systems such as those in Hong Kong, Italy, and Japan that use waste water and seawater when pure water is not needed.

Tomorrow's water-consuming equipment (5), such as washing machines, will waste much less water. Many such machines could run perfectly well on partly treated waste water instead of water of drinking quality.

Warm waste water from factories (6) could be piped to greenhouses or fish ponds, reducing river pollution.

Farming – the biggest consumer of water – and industry both need to apply less wasteful methods of using water. These include better irrigation control in farming, and in industry more recycling of waste materials – which often saves water – and of waste water itself.

Today we pump a lot of water from pure underground sources, or purify other supplies, before using it for activities that do not need the cleanest water, including toilet flushing, clothes washing, crop irrigation, and many purposes in factories. Tomorrow's towns and cities could have systems – already developed on a small scale – that save the purest water for important uses, such as in kitchens and hospitals, while meeting other needs with less pure, "recycled" water, or even seawater. Without such changes we could all face major water shortages in the not-too-distant future.

PRESENTING DATA

This book uses a wide variety of diagrams and maps to present many kinds of information. Maps are an important feature of an atlas, and in this book they take various forms and present data in a range of different ways. Many of the maps are combined with other kinds of diagram.

The purpose of using maps and diagrams is to convey information in a clear, visually interesting, yet straightforward way. Diagrams that need long, complicated explanations are not much help. But well-designed graphics can often communicate information more clearly than a lot of words.

Here we look at the various forms of diagram used in the book. Some of these examples – from simple bar charts to combined maps and pictograms – appear in earlier chapters. We explain how each sort of diagram works and the kind of information that it is most suitable for.

Bar charts are useful for comparing things. The height of the bar shows an amount. The example here presents three kinds of information for one country, which can then be compared with others. Bar charts can also be horizontal.

Histograms are graphs with bars to represent measurements of the same item at different stages. This shows the proportion of the total population of each age.

Maps and histograms can be combined (left). Here targets for reducing carbon dioxide emissions are compared.

Line graphs such as that below show how some sets of information are related to others over time. Often these graphs have more than one line, and they may include different but relevant information.

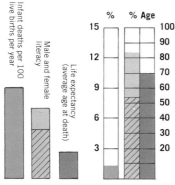

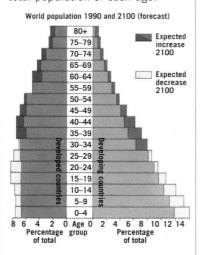

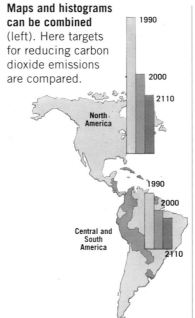

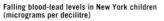

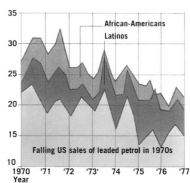

Pie charts show the proportions of several items that make up a whole. The area of each slice of the "pie" represents the size of the share. In this example the segments indicate how much of a continent's total area is covered by crops, animal grazing, forest, and other land.

Exploded, three-dimensional pie charts help to show the size of each segment more clearly, and emphasize information about volume or weight. In this case we can see that nearly a third of the total world fish catch in 1990, weighing 97 million tonnes, was used for animal feed and fertilizer.

Comparative pie charts bring together similar sets of data. In our example each pie represents a different amount of discharge. The segments within the pies allow us to compare each pollutant's path via New York City's river estuary to the sea in the 1980s (before discharges were banned).

Pie charts can draw attention to important points. This three-dimensional diagram strikingly illustrates how much less water a Bangladeshi villager uses each day (35 litres) than a UK city dweller (200 litres).

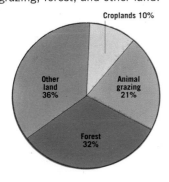

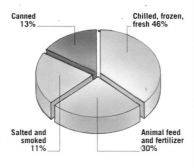

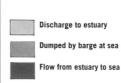

Pictograms (pictorial diagrams) use pictures to represent data. They are best for giving simple information. This pictogram compares the size of four fleets of factory-fishing ships, measured by tonnage (the maximum weight of fish that the fleet can carry at one time).

Liberia 20,000 tonnes

Panama 50,000 tonnes

Japan 200,000 tonnes

Former Soviet Union 8,000,000 tonnes

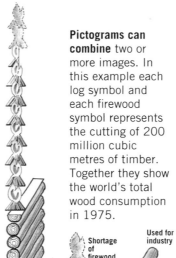

Pictograms can combine two or more images. In this example each log symbol and each firewood symbol represents the cutting of 200 million cubic metres of timber. Together they show the world's total wood consumption in 1975.

Shortage of firewood

Used for industry

Used for firewood

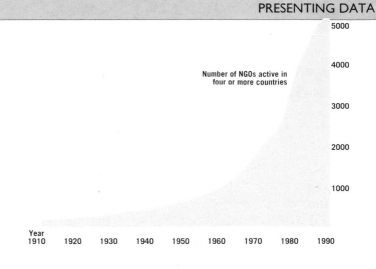

Number of NGOs active in four or more countries

Year
1910 1920 1930 1940 1950 1960 1970 1980 1990

5000
4000
3000
2000
1000

The "curve" of a line graph links many separate points and tells us about the speed of change over time. The steepening curve of this graph shows that the number of international non-governmental organizations (NGOs) grew faster than ever in the late 1970s and early 1980s, then levelled off slightly.

Maps can present a huge range of data in addition to purely geographical information. The example here compares how women were represented in the legislatures (law-making bodies) of different countries in the 1980s.

Not all adults can vote

Women as a proportion of members of legislature

No information
Less than 10%
11%–20%
21%–30%
31%–40%

Maps and pictograms can be combined to good effect. This map shows the state of the nuclear industry in Europe (excluding the former Soviet Union) in 1982 and 1990. To understand the map fully, we need to study the key first. Then it becomes clear at a glance which countries have most nuclear reactors, which built reactors during the 1980s, which rely most on nuclear power, and where nuclear accidents have occurred.

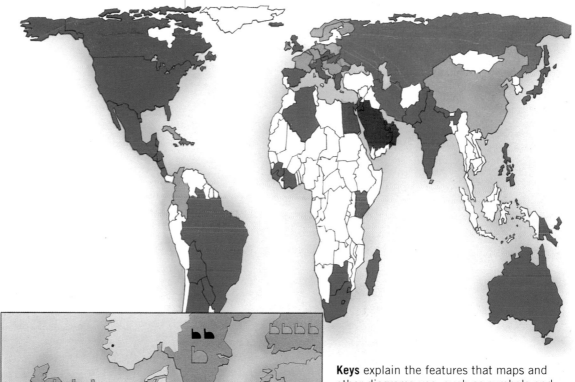

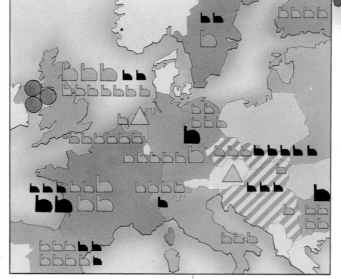

Keys explain the features that maps and other diagrams use, such as symbols and shading. In this case, the map uses the nuclear power station symbol in different sizes and colours to present a range of information.

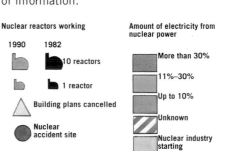

Nuclear reactors working

1990   1982

10 reactors

1 reactor

Building plans cancelled

Nuclear accident site

Amount of electricity from nuclear power

More than 30%
11%–30%
Up to 10%
Unknown
Nuclear industry starting

43

FURTHER READING

MAGAZINES
BBC Wildlife (monthly)
Bird Life (6 issues a year)
Earth Matters (4 issues a year)
Ecologist (6 issues a year)
Environment Digest (10 issues a year)
Ethical Consumer (6 issues a year)
Geography Review (monthly)
National Geographic (monthly)
Nature (weekly)
Natural History (monthly)
New Internationalist (monthly)
New Scientist (weekly)
Oxfam News (4 issues a year)
Permaculture Magazine (4 issues a year)
Resurgence (6 issues a year)

GENERAL REFERENCE FOR YOUNG PEOPLE
Miranda Ashwell, *Foundation Geography in Action*, books 1–3, Heinemann Educational, 1996.
Atlas of the Environment, Wayland, 1994.
David Bedds, *The Third World: Development and Interdependence*, Oxford University Press, 1995 edn.
Martyn Bramwell, *Planet Earth*, Kingfisher, 1991.
David Burnie, *How Nature Works*, Dorling Kindersley Eyewitness, 1991.
Margaret Burr, *We Have Always Lived Here: The Maya of Guatemala*, Minority Rights Group, 1991.
Children of the World, Rescue Mission Planet Earth: A Children's Edition of Agenda 21, Kingfisher and United Nations, 1994.
Conflicts series, Wayland.
Conserving our World series, Wayland.
Wendy Davies, *Closing the Borders*, Wayland *Global Issues* series, 1995.
Economically Developing Countries series, Wayland, 1994.
John Elkington and Julia Hailes, *The Young Green Consumer Guide*, Gollancz, 1990.
John Farndon, *Dictionary of the Earth*, Dorling Kindersley, 1994.
John Farndon, *How the Earth Works*, Dorling Kindersley Eyewitness, 1992.
Finding Out About series, Watts Books: titles on conservation and development, farming, urban environment, waste management.
David Flint, *Europe and the Environment*, Wayland, 1991.
Friends of the Earth, *Discovering the Environment* leaflet series: environmental issues and solutions. *Mad About* leaflet/poster series: topical environmental issues. Friends of the Earth teaching packs: titles include *Action on the Environment, Discovering*

Tropical Rainforests, Energy and the Environment, Green your School, Lasting Harvest: New Directions in World Farming, Right up your Street: Recycling, and *Your Home, your Planet*.
Nance Fyson, *Rich World, Poor World*, Oxford University Press, 1991.
Teresa Garlake, *The Rich-Poor Divide, Global Issues* series, Wayland, 1995.
Sue Grabham (ed.), *The Kingfisher Encyclopedia of Lands and Peoples*, Kingfisher, 1995.
Green Issues series, Watts Books.
Tony Hare, *Toxic Waste*, Gloucester Books, 1991.
Human Rights series, Wayland.
Issues for the Nineties series, Independence Publishers: titles on population, racial discrimination, poverty.
Edward Johnson, *United Nations – Peacekeeper?*, Wayland *Global Issues* series, 1995.
Alex Johnston with Jonathon Porritt, *Lifelines: Letters to Change the World*, Red Fox and Friends of the Earth, 1995.
Tim King, *Ecology*, Nelson, 1995 edn.
Brian Knapp, *Lands of the South: A Study of Third World Development*, Longman, 1995.
Brian Knapp, *World Geography* series, Atlantic Europe Publishing, 1994–95.
W.E. and V.M. Marsden, *World Concerns*, Longman, 1995.
Fred Martin, *Focus on Disasters* series, Heinemann Educational, 1996.
Fred Martin, *Themes in Geography* series, Heinemann Educational, 1996: includes title on environmental change.
F.M. Mayers and M.J. Readman, *The Dynamic World*, Longman, 1996.
Our World series, Wayland.
People and Places series, Wayland.
Philip's Environment Atlas, Heinemann Educational in association with the World Wide Fund for Nature, 3rd edn, 1996.
Points of View series, Wayland.
Steve Pollock, *Ecology*, Dorling Kindersley Eyewitness, 1994.
Stephen Sterling and Sue Lyle, *The Global Environment*, Longman, 1996.
Jenny Tesar, *Endangered Habitats*, Facts on File, 1992
Threatened Cultures series, Wayland: titles on Aborigines, Bedouin, Bushmen, Inuit, Kurds, Maori, Native Americans, Rainforest Amerindians, Saami, Tibetans.
Lloyd Timberlake, *Famine in Africa*, Franklin Watts, 1990.
Jane Walker, *Atmosphere in Danger*,

Gloucester Press, 1993.
Rachel Warner (ed.), *African Voices: From Angola, Sudan, Uganda, and Zaire*, Minority Rights Group, 1995.
Rachel Warner (ed.), *Voices: From Eritrea, Somalia, and Kurdistan*, Minority Rights Group, 1991.
David Waugh, *The Wider World*, Nelson, 1994.
Wayland Library of Science and Technology series, Wayland, 1994
Lawrence Williams, *Famine and Hunger*, Cloverleaf, 1992
World Environment Atlas, Collins and Longman, 1993.
World Focus series, Heinemann Educational and Oxfam, 1994–96: titles on Bagladesh, Brazil, Ethiopia, and nine other countries.
Young People of the World, A World in our Hands: In Honour of the 50th Anniversary of the United Nations, Tricycle (Berkeley, USA) and Peace Child International, 1995.

An annual *Resources for Schools and Youth Groups* catalogue is available from Oxfam (for address and telephone number, see page 183). This lists materials from a wide range of publishers and other organizations. These include:
Backbone of Development, 1994.
Be my Guest: An Introduction to Tourism's Impact, Tourism Concern.
Can You Be Different?, 1994.
Changing Places, Oxfam, 1991.
The Coffee Chain Game, 1994.
Colonialism, Conflict and Community, 1994.
Dammed Water: Nigeria, IBT, 1995
Developing Geography: Ghana, 1995.
Doing It Ourselves.
Education for Development, Hodder & Stoughton and UNICEF, 1995.
Fala Favela, Catholic Fund for Overseas Development, 1991.
The Final Frontier? Land, Environment and Pastoralism in Kenya, 1994.
Mangla: A Study of Change and Development in Mirpur, Azad and Kashmir, Pakistan, 1995.
Moving Stories: A Young Person's Guide to Refugees in Today's World, British Red Cross, 1995.
Peters Projection World Map.
Refugees: We Left Because We Had To, Refugee Council, 1995.
A Right to a Roof, Council for Education in World Citizenship, 1994.
Shifting Sands: Agriculture, Development, and Environmental Change in India's Thar Desert, 1994.
Southern Perspectives on Development, 1996.
Summing up the World: Mathematical Activities with a Global Perspective.

The Trading Game, Christian Aid, 1993.
Triumph of Hope: Eritrea's Struggle for Development, 1994.
Understanding Global Issues.
"We All Have the Right . . .", poster set, 1995.
Where We Live, Birmingham DEC, 1992.
Women Make a Difference, poster set, Oxfam, 1993.
Worlds behind the Music, 1995.

YOUNG PEOPLE'S FICTION, MYTH, AND POETRY RELATED TO THE ENVIRONMENT

Judy Allen, *Awaiting Developments*, Walker, 1989.
Melvin Burgess, *Baby and Fly Pie*, Andersen, 1993.
Jennifer Curry, *The Last Rabbit*, Mammoth, 1990: poetry.
Paula Danziger, *Earth to Matthew*, Heinemann, 1991.
Anita Desai, *The Village by the Sea*, Heinemann, 1982.
Peter Dickinson, *AK*, Gollancz, 1990.
Nicholas Fisk, *A Hole in the Head*, Walker, 1991.
Anne Harvey, *Shades of Green*, Julia Macrae, 1991: poetry.
Gaye Hicilmaz, *Against the Storm*, Viking, 1990.
Ho Minfong, *Rice without Rain*, Heinemann, 1989.
Lesley Howarth, *Weather Eye*, Walker, 1995.
Monica Hughes, *The Crystal Drop*, Methuen, 1992.
Ted Hughes, *The Iron Woman*, Faber, 1993.
Robert Hull, *Breaking Free: An Anthology of Human Rights*, Wayland, 1994: poetry.
Rosalind Kernen (ed.), *The Rain Forest Story Book: Traditional Stories from the Original Forest Peoples of South America, Africa, and Southeast Asia*, Cambridge University Press, 1994.
Elizabeth Laird, *Kiss the Dust*, Heinemann, 1991.
Michael Morpurgo, *Why the Whales Came*, Heinemann, 1985
Beverley Naidoo, *Chain of Fire*, Collins, 1989.
Michael Rosen (ed.), *South and North, East and West*, Walker, 1992.
Graham Salisbury, *Blue Skin of the Sea*, Scholastic, 1994.
Nikki Siagen-Smith (ed.), *Songs for Survival: Songs and Chants from Tribal Peoples around the World*, Barefoot Books and Survival International, 1995.
Robert Swindells, *Brother in the Land*, Oxford University Press, 1984.
Anthony Wall, *The Eden Mission*, Robinswood Press, 1995.

ADULT BOOKS

Frank Barnaby (ed.), *The Gaia Peace Atlas*, Pan Books, 1988.
John Barraclough and Dave Dalton, *One Earth, Two Worlds*, Oxfam, 1995.
Julian Berger, *The Gaia Atlas of First Peoples*, Robertson McCarta, 1990.
Rachel Carson, *Silent Spring*, Penguin Books, 1965.
Karen Christensen, *The Green Home: How to Make your World a Better Place*, Piatkus, 1995.
Michael Cranna (ed.), *The True Cost of Conflict*, Earthscan and Saferworld, 1995
Cultural Survival, *State of the Peoples: A Global Human Rights Report on Societies in Danger*, Beacon Press (Boston, USA), 1993.
Nigel Dudley and Sue Stickland, *G Is for ecoGarden: An A-Z Guide to an Organically Healthy Garden*, Gaia Books, 1991.
Lee Durrell, *Gaia State of the Ark Atlas*, Gaia Books, 1986.
Paul Ekins, *Wealth beyond Measure: An Atlas of New Economics*, Gaia Books, 1992.
Marianne Frances, *Small Change: A Pocketful of Practical Actions to Help the Environment*, Merlin Press, 1993.
Friends of the Earth, *How to Be a Friend of the Earth*, 1991.
Friends of the Earth, *Take the Heat off the Planet: How You Can Really Help Stop Climate Change*, 1993.
Friends of the Earth, *Your Countryside Is under Threat*, 1994.
Herbert Girardet, *The Gaia Atlas of Cities: New Directions for Sustainable Urban Living*, Gaia Books, 1995.
Peter Harper, Jeremy Light, and Chris Madsen, *The Natural Garden Book*, Gaia Books, 1994.
Roger Hart, *The Children's Community Participation Handbook: Involving Children in Sustainable Development*, Earthscan and UNICEF, 1996
Anthony Huxley, *Green Inheritance: The WWF Book of Plants*, Gaia Books, 1994.
Anna Kruger, *H Is for ecoHome: An A-Z Guide to a Healthier, Planet-Friendly Household*, Gaia Books, 1991.
Miles Litvinoff, *The Earthscan Action Handbook for People and Planet*, Earthscan, 1990.
James Lovelock, *Gaia: The Practical Science of Planetary Medicine*, Gaia Books, 1991.
Jan McHarry, *Reuse, Repair, Recycle: A Mine of Creative Ideas for Thrifty Living*, Gaia Books, 1993.
Norman Myers (ed.), *The Gaia Atlas of Planet Management*, Gaia Books, 1994 edn.
Arno Peters, *The Peters Atlas of the World*, Longman, 1995.
David Sattherthwaite and others, *The*

Environment for Children: Understanding and Acting on the Environmental Hazards That Threaten Children and their Parents, Earthscan, 1996.
Joni Seager, *The State of the Environment Atlas*, Penguin Books, 1995.
Pat Simmons, *Words into Action: Basic Rights and the Campaign against World Poverty*, Oxfam, 1995.
Ted Trainer, *Towards a Sustainable Economy: The Need for Fundamental Change*, Jon Carpenter, 1996.
UNICEF, *The State of the World's Children 1996*, Oxford University Press, 1995.
Kevin Watkins, *The Oxfam Poverty Report*, Oxfam, 1995.
Phil Wells and Mandy Jetter, *The Global Consumer: Best Buys to Help the Third World*, Gollancz and New Consumer, 1991.
World Development Movement, *The Great Aid Robbery: How British Aid Fails the Poor*, 1995.

CD-ROM SOFTWARE

The Big Green Disc. Looks at major environmental issues, such as global warming and pollution.
Encarta '95 (Microsoft). An all-embracing encyclopedia.
Energy Resources (Bradford Technology) Investigates energy sources and uses.
Exploring Plant Sciences (Attica Cybernetics) Survey of the plant kingdom and uses of plants.
ITN European Atlas (Attica Cybernetics) Maps and country profiles.
Last Chance to See (Softline). The record of a search for endangered species.
Lifemap series (Time Warner Interactive). Focuses on different major groups of animals.
Mammals (National Geographic Society) An encyclopedia of 400 mammals with text, photographs, and film clips.
Nature in Motion (Andromeda). A voyage through the world's natural habitats.
Ocean Life (Suneria Educational). Explores marine wildlife.
Sim City 2000 (Interplay Ltd). Plan your own city of the future – a simulation game.
World Guide (Third World Institute and Oxfam). Statistics and texts on global issues and the world's countries compiled by researchers and journalists in developing countries. Also available in book form.
World Reference Atlas (Dorling Kindersley). Country profiles and gazetteer.
Zoo Guides (Kim Tec). The world's wildlife, including many endangered species.
Worldwatch Database Disk 1996 (Worldwatch Institute). Graphs, tables, and data on the state of our planet and human environmental impacts.

GLOSSARY

Acid Any one of a group of liquid chemicals that eat away solid materials.

Acid rain Cloud, mist, rain, sleet, or snow that forms when acidic waste gases from fuel burning combine with water in the atmosphere.

Acidification An increase in the acidity of soil or water.

Alternative energy Another name for renewable energy.

Aquifer Underground rocks holding water.

Atmosphere The thin layer of gases surrounding the Earth.

Atom The smallest known part of any chemical that can combine with another chemical.

Bauxite The clay ore from which people obtain aluminium.

Biodegradable Able to decompose naturally.

Biogas Fuel gas made from plants or rotting refuse.

Cancer A harmful tumour or growth that may spread from one part of the body to others.

Carbon dioxide A gas combining carbon and oxygen, produced by living things during respiration (e.g. through breathing), the rotting of organic matter, and the burning of fuels. .

Carcinogen A cancer-causing substance.

Catalytic converter A device fitted to the exhaust of a motor vehicle to reduce the flow of waste gases into the air.

CFCs Chlorofluorocarbons, the main ozone-destroying chemicals. They are human-made and do not occur in nature.

CHP Combined heat and power, a way of using fuel in power stations more efficiently by making use of waste heat produced there.

Climate The usual weather conditions of an area.

Conservation The protection and management of natural resources and the environment.

Consumption The act of using up a resource or product.

Continent One of the Earth's large landmasses.

Crust The rigid outer part of the Earth.

DDT Dichloro-diphenol-trichloroethane, one of the earliest and strongest chemical pesticides, linked with some cancers and damage to wildlife, and now banned in developed countries.

Deposit Any material that has been set down, such as silt or coal.

Developed country A country where large-scale industry, based on the burning of fossil fuels, is well established and usually the main source of jobs and wealth creation.

Developing country A country where farming, rather than large-scale industry, is still the main way of life.

Development Growth or progress; in economics, change whereby a community or a country becomes more effective at meeting its needs.

Dioxins A dangerous group of human-made chemicals, usually the by-products of other processes.

Dumping Unloading or disposing of a substance.

Emission The discharge of any substance into the environment.

Energy efficiency Ways of producing and using energy from fuels that reduce waste to a minimum.

Environment The surroundings in which a plant or animal lives.

Equator An imaginary line around the surface of the Earth at an equal distance from the north and south poles.

Estuary The mouth of a river where fresh and sea water mix.

Evaporate To rise up in small droplets (vapour) into the air.

Export To sell to another country.

Food chain A series of plants and animals, each of which serves as food for the next "up" the chain.

Fossil fuels Coal, natural gas, and oil, created over millions of years by the decay of plant and animal remains.

Fuel Any substance burned to produce heat or power.

Fuelwood Firewood.

Geothermal Related to heat inside the Earth.

Glacier A large, slow-moving mass of ice, formed from the compaction (firm pressing together) of snow on high ground, that flows down a valley.

Global warming The probable raising of average temperatures on the Earth caused by the greenhouse effect.

Greenhouse effect The trapping of the Sun's heat close to the Earth by gases in the atmosphere.

Greenhouse gas Any gas that assists the greenhouse effect.

Groundwater Underground water.

Half-life The time taken by radioactive materials to lose half their radioactivity.

Heavy metal A metal that can be converted from one form to another but not destroyed.

Hemisphere Half the Earth, divided north and south, or east and west.

HFCs Hydrofluorocarbons, non-ozone-destroying replacement chemicals for CFCs.

High-tech Using up-to-date, complicated technology.

Hydroelectricity The use of the power of falling or running water to produce electricity.

Ice cap A thick mass of ice or snow permanently covering the land.

Import To buy from another country.

Incineration The burning of refuse or other materials in a specially built furnace.

Industrial Revolution The 18th- and 19th-century development of large-scale industrial manufacturing in the countries of Western Europe and North America.

Industry Organized activity concerned with the processing of raw materials to produce things that people use, including food.

Infant mortality The rate of death among young children.

Infection An invasion of the body by harmful microbes.

Insulation A barrier to the movement of heat, sound, or electricity.

Irrigation The supply of water to farmland to improve crop growth.

Kilowatt 1000 watts.

Kilowatt-hour Energy equal to the work done by 1000 watts in one hour.

Landfill The disposal of solid waste materials by burying them in the ground.

Malaria A dangerous infectious disease carried by mosquitoes.

Manufacturing Making products, especially factory goods, from raw materials.

Mineral Any solid, non-plant and non-animal, naturally occurring material.

North The developed countries of Western Europe, North America, Japan, and Australasia.

Nuclear Related to the nucleus, the centre of an atom.

Nuclear energy Energy production based on using changes in the centre of atoms to generate heat.

Nuclear reactor The central part of a nuclear power station where nuclear energy is produced.

Nuclear waste The unwanted by-products of nuclear energy production.

Ore Rock containing a useful mineral.

Organic Living.

Ozone A form of oxygen naturally present in the Earth's upper

atmosphere, and also produced by a mixture of polluting gases in the lower atmosphere.
Ozone layer The layer of ozone in the Earth's upper atmosphere that filters out ultraviolet rays from the Sun.

PCBs Polychlorinated biphenyls, indestructible, dangerous human-made chemicals.
Percent(age) Out of every 100.
Photosynthesis The process by which plants use the Sun's energy to make their own food from carbon dioxide and water, releasing oxygen as a by-product of the process.
Plutonium A radioactive substance produced in nuclear reactors and used in the manufacture of nuclear weapons.
Pollution Any substance that interferes with and harms natural processes when added to the natural environment.

Radiation Electromagnetic rays – from short wavelength rays such as x rays, to long wavelength rays such as radio waves, and including light – and particles that travel through space. The high-energy forms of radiation, such as x-rays, can pass through most materials.
Radioactive The quality of giving out atomic radiation.
Raw material A naturally occurring substance used to make something else.
Recycling Using or processing materials (or energy) more than once.
Renewable Able to be used without reducing stocks of natural resources or causing pollution.
Renewable energy Energy that can be produced using natural processes such as tidal and wave movements, river flow, wind, and sunshine.
Reserve An area set aside for conservation of habitats and species; or the quantity of a resource that people know is

available for use at reasonable cost.
Resource A naturally occurring substance (such as a mineral deposit) or process (such as water flow) that provides materials or energy for people to use.

Sanitation Equipment and facilities used to protect public health, especially with regard to toilets and water supplies.
Sewage Waste matter carried away in sewers and drains.
Smog Air pollution caused by the mixture of smoke and fog.
Solar Connected with the Sun.
South The developing countries of Africa, Asia, the Caribbean, Central and South America, and the Pacific.

Thermal Connected with heat.
Tidal power Energy generated using the rise and fall of tides.
Toxin, toxic Poison, poisonous.
Tropics The high-temperature regions of the Earth's surface to the north and south of the equator.
Turbine A machine driven by liquid, steam, gas, or air pressure to produce energy.

Ultraviolet An invisible form of radiation that can tan and burn exposed human skin.
UV Ultraviolet.

Vapour A mass of small droplets of a liquid in the air.
Vegetation Living plants.

INDEX

Headwords refer to information in texts and captions but not maps. **Bold** page numbers refer to main entries in text.